MIRACLE DRUG

MIRACLE DRUG

THE INNER HISTORY
OF PENICILLIN

By

DAVID MASTERS

1946

EYRE & SPOTTISWOODE

LONDON

OPPOSITE: *Professor Sir Howard Florey, the leader of the team of Oxford scientists who surmounted incredible difficulties before they isolated penicillin and proved it to be the most wonderful drug hitherto discovered by man.*

DEDICATED

TO

ALL THOSE SCIENTISTS
WHOSE DEVOTED WORK PRODUCED PENICILLIN
TO AID SUFFERING HUMANITY

Contents

List of Illustrations

FOREWORD

The award of the Nobel Prize in October, 1945, to Sir Alexander Fleming, Sir Howard Florey and Dr. E. B. Chain for their work on penicillin confirmed the fact that this was one of the greatest discoveries in medical science ever made in the history of mankind.

That the lowly fungus known as *Penicillium notatum* possessed the power to save human life was revealed only recently; that it could produce a drug which in its purified form possessed a potency of such immense strength that one part in 100,000,000 would prevent the growth of sensitive germs was bordering on the unbelievable; that the main secret was eventually wrested from his humble mould by the team of Oxford scientists of whom Sir Howard Florey was the inspiration and leader was something in the nature of a miracle. But it was not wrought by pressing a button or waving a magic wand. It was achieved by the application of scientific knowledge and the unremitting toil of many brilliant scientists and above all by their refusal to be beaten by difficulties which seemed to be insuperable. Because they refused to accept defeat, all Mankind in the ages to come will be blessed with the life-saving gift of penicillin until the glad day dawns when human beings are endowed with sufficient intelligence and knowledge so to order their lives that the germs which now exact a deadly toll will be rendered harmless by the shield of healthy immunity which education and understanding will conjure up in a world bespangled with beauty, though it is at present sullied by folly and ignorance.

My aim in writing this work was to tell how the miracle of penicillin was slowly accomplished from that historic moment when Sir Alexander Fleming observed its first manifestation until Sir Howard Florey and Dr. Chain and their colleagues gazed upon the speck of powder in which lay hidden a small trace of pure penicillin. American workers made their contributions to the later developments; but this unique discovery was purely a British discovery, and in seeking to unfold every aspect of this fascinating story I have travelled far and seen many scientists whose unfailing courtesy and help I hereby acknowledge. I also wish to thank those British and American manufacturers and officials without whose aid this authoritative book could not have been completed.

Dr. Charles Thom, the famous American mycologist, published in *Mycologia* a list of eleven conspicuous microbial enemies of man that were sensitive to penicillin. "Such a list justifies the caption 'miracle drug' put upon it by another medical scholar who is rarely swayed by impulse," he wrote, and thereby gave me justification for selecting this title for my book.

DAVID MASTERS.

CHAPTER I

THE BATTLE OF GERMS

MEDICAL SCIENCE contains many fascinating stories, but none more fascinating than that of penicillin, in which pure chance, acute observation, good luck and bad luck, brilliant work and incredible difficulties were all mixed up in the most amazing way. The hunt for penicillin was like hunting a will o' the wisp. Four times it nearly succeeded and each time the precious substance eluded the men who sought to track it down. For years the quest was dropped. Then it was taken up again by a group of scientists at Oxford who, fighting through a maze of difficulties, at length gave to suffering humanity one of the greatest boons in the history of medicine.

Some medical discoveries, with no sign to point the way, have opened up new fields of knowledge never before conceived by the human mind, such as Harvey's discovery of the circulation of the blood in the beginning of the sixteenth century, Antony von Leeuwenhoek's discovery in 1682 of micro-organisms in his own mouth, Pasteur's discovery, during his studies on the fermentation of beer and wine, of the invisible living organisms which floated in the air and which led him twenty years later in April, 1878, to publish his theory that all diseases were caused by microscopic organisms— this marked the foundation of modern bacteriology as surely as Manson's discovery of the way in which the mosquito infected man with the parasite of filaria provided the key which opened up the whole field of tropical medicine and led to further discoveries that incriminated insects and lice and ticks as the carriers of diseases from which millions of human beings suffered and died.

But penicillin, despite the wonder of it, was not like these. It was in 1898, some thirty years before Fleming made his first observation, that a scientist named Gosio began the pioneer researches on moulds by experimenting with one known as *Penicillium brevi-compactum*— because its sporing organ was so short and compact—and obtained from it a substance called mycophenolic acid. Had Gosio been able to produce it in sufficient quantities, he would have carried out experiments on animals, for he was interested in anthrax. But he could obtain so little of the acid that he was unable to do what he had in mind, so he tested it in the laboratory upon some anthrax bacilli which usually grew at an amazing rate when sown upon their normal medium, pushing out thread after thread until the flask was a felted mass. With keen interest he saw that by adding his new acid to the medium, the mad multiplication of the anthrax germs was stopped and they ceased to grow—to use the favourite term of the scientist, their growth was inhibited.

Not until fifteen years later, in 1913, did Alsberg and Black produce more of this acid from the mould and discover that they could inject it into mice without harming them. Then they extracted from another mould named *Penicillium puberulum* an acid which they called penicillic acid and succeeded in obtaining it in crystal form. Experimenting with this in the laboratory upon the *bacillus coli*, a germ which is common in the human intestine, they found it was possible to stop the bacillus from growing; but unfortunately it was quite useless for human treatment, because it was poisonous to animals.

Obviously moulds were beginning to arouse some interest, for that same year Vaudremer tested another mould named *Aspergillus fumigatus* which he believed might be helpful to those people suffering from the dread disease of tuberculosis. His experiments disclosed that some of the liquid in which this mould was cultured would eventually bring about the destruction of the *tubercle bacillus* growing in the test tube and, fortified by this knowledge, he injected some of the liquid into patients suffering from tuberculosis. Whatever hope Vaudremer may have had of curing tuberculosis, the fact that the treatment was discontinued indicates clearly that the early hopes were not fulfilled. From the mould with which Vaudremer experimented in 1913, the biochemist has since isolated four different substances known as gliotoxin, helvolic acid, spinulosin and fumigatin and all can now be obtained in the form of crystals. Each exerts a strong antibacterial action against certain germs, so Vaudremer had considerable scientific justification for using the products of the mould to attempt to cure man, although he was quite unable in his day to isolate the different substances the fungus produced. Incidentally it is interesting to know that another strain of *Aspergillus* is largely used by chemical manufacturers to produce the immense quantities of citric acid consumed in the form of synthetic lemonade and flavourings and used in commercial processes all over the world.

Thus a worker here and there began to take a scientific interest in those moulds which are sometimes found growing on top of a jar of jam when it is opened, or which develops upon a pair of wet shoes if they happen to be thrown into a cupboard and neglected. Such moulds are usually a great nuisance because they spoil and ruin so many things in the way of food and fabrics and leather. For instance, when my house was destroyed by bombing, one of my carpets upon recovery was saturated with rain and smothered in lime from the fallen ceiling. The cleaners at the moment were so overwhelmed with work that none could be found to deal with it, so it was dumped in a cellar until it could be collected. A week later someone chanced to touch the carpet and, finding it hot, remarked: "They must have a fire down below here."

Instantly I realized the truth. "It's not a fire. It's the carpet heating up," I exclaimed.

Dragging it forth, I opened it out, to find there was a mould with whiskers half an inch long over the greater part of it. Luckily I was able to dry it and save it before too much damage was done. But had it remained in the cellar much longer it would have been completely destroyed by the mould, for the closely packed layers of soddened wool and jute, heavily charged with dust and lime, provided ideal conditions for the growth of the fungus which spontaneously generated heat.

It seems difficult to realize that these moulds which are so destructive may be put to work to produce substances that are of the greatest benefit to humanity, yet we have only to think of penicillin to know that this is true.

The idea of using one germ to fight and destroy another goes back even earlier than the idea of using the products of moulds to try to cure disease, for it has exercised the minds of scientists on and off ever since Pasteur and Joubert discovered in 1877 that the anthrax bacillus, which wrought such havoc among French flocks and herds, could be neutralized and destroyed by bacteria which float about in the air. Thus Pasteur started a never-ending search for organisms that were antagonistic to each other. Many a bacteriologist has since carried out researches in his laboratory with different germs in the hope of finding a harmless germ that would cure human disease and such work has added a deal of knowledge to the subject of microbial antagonism.

In 1887, ten years after Pasteur published his results, a Swiss named Garré was inspired to attempt something new in his efforts to help humanity. His idea was to prepare some glass plates by coating them with nutrient gelatine, then with a platinum loop to smear different bacteria in parallel lines across the plates, leaving a slight gap between the lines of germs. He reasoned quite logically that if his lines of germs were to deposit anything in the layer of gelatine, it would spread out until it came into contact with the lines of germs on each side, when it would be quite easy to see if the stuff which diffused out was able to prevent the adjacent bacteria from growing. It became possible in this way to test simultaneously a number of different bacteria on the same plate and so save the time and labour of preparing a different plate for each different organism. This new idea which Garré gave to the science of bacteriology was to play its part forty years later when penicillin was first tested in the laboratory in a similar manner.

Numerous experiments along these and other lines to discover microbial antagonisms started in hope and ended in disappointment. But knowledge continued to grow and scientists learned as much from their failures as from their successes. Now a number of workers began to concentrate upon anthrax. The reason for this was not far to seek, for the memory was still fresh of Pasteur's triumph at Melun in 1881 when he risked his reputation and proved to the world that he had found the way to vaccinate sheep to render them immune against this fatal fever. Emmerich, working quietly in Germany, announced that he had protected rabbits against the disease by giving them an injection containing a streptococcus. Another German scientist named Doehle went a step further. He was not content to allow men to judge his work by a verbal description of his experiments, so he published visual evidence in the form of a photograph to prove that he could prevent the growth of the anthrax bacillus by using something produced by a germ to which he gave the resounding name of *Micrococcus anthracotoxicus*—in common English it means the very small coccus which is poisonous to anthrax. It may be explained that the cocci are round in shape, resembling infinitely tiny globes, and if the pneumococci which cause pneumonia be stained and examined through a microscope they appear as a myriad of tiny blue dots peppered all over the slide. The bacilli, on the other hand, resemble minute sausages.

While Emmerich and Doehle were pursuing their own lines of research with the cocci, a French scientist, Bouchard, was experimenting in his laboratory with the *Bacillus pyocyaneus* which he injected into his test animals at the same time that he injected the anthrax germs. He was quite pleased with the results, for if the animals developed any fever at all, it was a slight attack from which they soon recovered, so he had no doubt that there was something in the *Bacillus pyocyaneus* which protected the animals. What it was he did not know.

For some years nobody bothered much about this bacillus. Then in 1898 Honl and Bukovsky determined to test it on human beings. Growing the germ on a considerable scale, they carefully filtered the medium to exclude all the bacilli, for they believed that the germ deposited something beneficial into the medium. Then they started to treat people who suffered from ulcers on the legs, soaking the bandages in the fluid and binding them in a saturated state over the ulcers. In the course of time they treated a hundred patients, some with ulcers so intractable to treatment that it looked as though the limbs would have to be amputated, yet the doctors reported that the fluid on which the bacilli were grown benefited all cases. They consequently developed their researches into a treatment which they subjected to a large scale test on men and women.

It was a year later that Emmerich and Low, who had been experimenting with this bacillus without knowing anything of the work of Honl and Bukovsky, announced that they had succeeded in obtaining from it a new substance called pyocyanase which possessed the power of dissolving the germs of anthrax and diphtheria. This product seemed to be very promising, and during the next few years pyocyanase was used by many continental physicians for the treatment of ulcers and boils, inflamed eyes and gonorrhoea. It became rather a vogue for about ten years. The physicians all spoke of favourable results, but the strange thing was that they gradually ceased to use it, although it continued to be produced commercially. Whether its decline in popularity was due to a falling off of its activity is not known, but significantly enough when the commercial product available in 1929 was subjected to a rigid laboratory test, it was found to lack all activity.

Thus ever since Pasteur first startled and shocked the medical world by his revolutionary theory that diseases were caused by germs, men have toiled with test tube and incubators and microscope to discover potent substances which microbes and moulds might be induced to yield in order to cure the illnesses or serve the purposes of mankind. The work of these pioneers serves as a sure guide to all who follow similar lines of research, and leads to a true appreciation of the remarkable story of penicillin.

CHAPTER II

FLEMING FINDS THE MOULD

DR. ALEXANDER FLEMING sat before a typewriter at a plain table in a small room opposite a public house in Paddington. The neighbourhood was drab. The impoverished people herded together in the grimy little houses and lived their hard lives while Dr. Fleming did his best to save them from dying. Traffic flowed in and out of Paddington Railway Station a few yards away as he gazed meditatively at his notes on the table and puffed away at his cigarette. Then he began to tap the keys again . . . "so for convenience and to avoid the repetition of the rather cumbersome phrase 'Mould broth filtrate' the name 'penicillin' will be used. This will denote the filtrate of a broth culture of the particular *penicillium* with which we are concerned."

So, in those days of 1929, sitting in his laboratory at St. Mary's Hospital in London composing his paper *On the Antibacterial Action of Cultures of a Penicillium with Special Reference to their Use in the Isolation of B. Influenzae*, Dr. Fleming wrote the word which at last echoed round the world until all civilized peoples were familiar with it.

His paper with the long words and longer title, which was received for publication on May 10, 1929, was published in the last ten pages of the June issue of *The British Journal of Experimental Pathology*, a technical journal for the student and specialist interested in pathology and bacteriology. There was no rush to read what he had written. The general public were completely ignorant of his paper. His observations were intended solely for those medical scientists who spent their days in studying germs. A few bacteriologists whose work familiarized them with the difficulty of obtaining a pure culture of any specific germ were attracted by the mention in the title of B. influenzae, otherwise Pfeiffer's influenza bacillus—which strangely enough is still linked with the name of influenza, although no specialist of our time would care to defend Pfeiffer's original claim that it caused the disease. Reading the paper, they were glad to note that Fleming had discovered a way of growing the influenza bacillus in a pure form, uncontaminated by any other germs, that if a plate were sown with a mixed infection of germs including the influenza bacillus, Fleming could kill off the unwanted germs and produce a plate with a fine healthy growth of the influenza bacillus alone. This was of great interest, for up till then it was as difficult to grow the influenza bacillus in a pure form from a mixed infection of germs as to grow a field of wheat without weeds; in fact the other germs generally overwhelmed the influenza bacillus and prevented its isolation; but the wonderful thing was that the broth made from the *penicillium* contained something which prevented several other germs from growing and allowed the influenza germs to flourish.

This may not seem very remarkable to the average man, but if he were given some seeds of brussels sprouts, cabbages, savoys and curly kale all mixed together and told that he must plant them in the same seed bed at the same time in such a way that, without touching the seedlings when they appeared, only the cabbages would grow, he might complain with reason that he was being asked to do the impossible. Yet Dr. Fleming could do something akin to that with germs and his paper told his fellow workers how he had accomplished this, in order that they could do likewise whenever they wanted to obtain a pure culture of the influenza bacillus for their experiments.

Fleming was a clear thinker who wrote concisely. His words, chosen with care, pointed out that the term penicillin denoted the filtered broth in which the mould was grown. It is now known that this bore no more resemblance to the highly purified forms of penicillin produced after years of arduous labour by the scientists at Oxford than gold quartz bears to pure gold, for just as gold quartz contains only a few grains of gold scattered through the rock, so the first filtrate of penicillin contained only a trace of penicillin mixed up with a large quantity of waste liquid. But that trace of penicillin was so potent that it made its influence felt. And Fleming was the first living man to detect the signs and sense the wonders to come.

The son of a farmer, Alexander Fleming was born in the farmhouse at Lochfield, a few miles from Darvel in Ayrshire, on August 6, 1881. It was a lonely farm, standing about 800 feet high on the side of a hill where the road came to an end amid the grass and stretches of heather which set the hills aflame in a blaze of purple when August merged into September. Like most Scottish farms, the farmhouse was solidly built of stone, while the farm spread over about two square miles of the moors where the sheep and cattle, which were the mainstay of the farmer, roved and grazed and grew fat for market. Trees were sparse. Behind the farmhouse the hill humped up for another three hundred feet, so the stranger who trudged to the top could truly claim to have climbed a mountain, although to the Fleming boys and girls it was always a hill. Over the hills to the east on the road to Strathaven lay Caldermill, while some fifteen miles to the west lay Kilmarnock, a few miles from Troon on the lovely firth of Clyde.

The Fleming family was large. There were five boys and three girls and here in the stone farmhouse with the smell of the byre in his nostrils and the bleating of the sheep on the hillsides Alexander Fleming spent his early days very close to nature. He played with the sheep dogs about the farm, watched the heather flame into beauty and die, saw the snow cover the countryside in a mantle of white as the smoke from the peats on the glowing fire tickled his nostrils. Then as the snow melted away into spring he observed the magical appearance of the baby lambs that frisked and frolicked about the moors in the most exciting way. But it was the stream, with the famous Ayrshire cattle grazing along its banks, that drew him most, for it abounded with trout that slid like shadows into the dim recesses of the pools and vanished in a flash of silver when a moving shadow fell on them from the bank. Nobody fished the stream, so he used to wander as a boy along its banks and spend hours pitting his skill against the wary trout.

"How did you fish them?" I asked.

"In every way you can think of," was the reply, with a reminiscent smile.

"With bent pins?" I inquired.

"No, not that way," he protested. "The trout were not very large, but they were very sweet. We could live on them in the summer," he added.

So young Alexander Fleming, rising early in the morning, would go down to the stream with rod and line to hook a few trout for breakfast or, lying in the heather in the sunny spring days, would mark the spots where the birds dropped to earth, so that he might seek their nests. As he grew older, he wandered about the farm, lending a hand where he could, going along to assist in cutting the peats and carting them up to the farm where he would help to stack them to dry ready for use when the cold weather came.

At eight years old his education began in earnest and he was sent to the nearest village school. It was four miles away and every morning about 8 o'clock he started to walk to school, his satchel containing his books along with a midday meal across his back; and every afternoon saw him setting out briskly for the four miles walk home. For three years, except during holidays, he cheerfully walked eight miles a day in pursuit of learning—unlike the Scottish child of 1944 whose parents insisted upon the local ratepayers paying 30s. a week for a taxicab to take their boy to and from another school not more than four miles distant. Rain or shine he walked, and many a day in starting out or returning home he was caught in an unexpected storm that soaked him to the skin. But he suffered no harm, and the walking developed his body and kept him fit and well.

He was eleven years old when he left the little school to broaden his mind and the basis of his education by attending Kilmarnock Academy. He studied diligently, and by the time he was thirteen years old his box was packed and he was sent off to live with his brother in London, where for the next two or three years he continued his education by attending the Polytechnic Institute in Regent Street. At that time he displayed no particular scientific ability, nor felt any urge to become a doctor. On the contrary, he sought his future livelihood in the world of shipping and found a job as office boy in Leadenhall Street at a wage that would shock the office boys of the present generation. Perhaps it was more dignified, more in keeping with the tradition of the great army of black-coated workers whose ranks he joined in the humblest capacity, to refer to him as a junior clerk. Very neatly dressed in a dark suit, he journeyed night and morning between Baker Street and Leadenhall Street, filling in the intervening time with the usual office routine, going on messages to the Baltic Exchange or to Lloyd's and lunching frugally at a city tea shop.

It was deadly dull. The close atmosphere of Leadenhall Street in the summer was oppressive to the young man who had filled his lungs with the invigorating air of Ayrshire and gaily walked his eight miles a day to and from school along the open country road. If the next two or three years brought increases in salary, they also brought a clearer understanding to Alexander Fleming. It may have been true that the streets of London were paved with gold, that fortunes were being made every day in the city of London, but to the young clerk the routine of the office was deadly, and after four years in the city a little legacy enabled him to throw up his job.

"Why did you leave?" I inquired.

"There were no prospects", was the quiet reply.

The brother with whom he lived had already taken his medical degree and was practising as a doctor. What was more natural than that the doctor should encourage his younger brother to go in for medicine too? Thus, at the age of twenty, Alexander Fleming became a student at the Medical School at St. Mary's Hospital in Paddington.

With all the preliminaries settled, he went off to St. Mary's Hospital to attend his first lectures at the Medical School, traversing the mean streets which he grew to know so well that in time he ceased to notice their drabness. Gradually, as the notes in his notebooks expanded and his theoretical knowledge grew, his eyes were opened in the hospital wards to the various diseases afflicting the men and women who entered for treatment, and he came to recognise how closely linked with disease were poverty and ignorance. Daily he saw what a blessed sanctuary the hospital offered to the poor people of the district who were stricken down with sickness.

There was no doubt that he had found his true bent, that medicine attracted him so much that his heart and soul were in it. His modesty tended to conceal his exceptional ability which took him to the top of his classes. He was a brilliant student. Working quietly, he took prize after prize with a scholarship or two, including the senior entrance scholarship in natural science to prove his outstanding merit. That all the branches of medical science appealed to him is indicated by the fact that he took honours in physiology, pharmacology, medicine, pathology, forensic medicine and hygiene, and he rounded off his work at St. Mary's Medical School in 1906 by winning the Gold Medal for Clinical Medicine. In 1908 he won the gold medal of London University when he took his degrees of Bachelor of Medicine and Bachelor of Science and the following year, at the age of twenty-eight, he became a Fellow of the Royal College of Physicians to crown at that period his distinguished academic career.

His life, crowded as it was with professional duties, was not entirely given up to work. He liked the company of his fellow Scots and, as he had joined the London Scottish as a private a year before he resigned from the shipping office in the city, he continued to belong to that gallant regiment and found time to attend their drills and parades. He looked forward to the annual camp, when he lived with them under canvas and slogged along the roads on their route marches. It was then that he reaped the full advantage of that regular eight mile a day walk as a schoolboy, for he often finished fresh when bigger men were overcome with fatigue. Though not big himself, being about five feet five inches tall, he was very agile, with broad shoulders and neat legs and feet, just the sort of man to pack a scrum. When the Bisley meeting came round he used to go down to shoot for the London Scottish Team and, although no King's Prizeman, he was a tolerable shot who made a fair score that won a prize or two. He enjoyed every minute of it and many a season his wavy brown hair could be seen blowing in the wind as he lay on the ranges with his rifle studying the strength of the gusts and the conditions of the target through his telescope.

In Fleming's student days there was a man at St. Mary's Hospital whose name was known in medical circles the world over. He was Dr. Almroth Wright who, as Sir Almroth Wright, was still Director of the Inoculation Department in 1946. Almroth Wright won his reputation by introducing a method of vaccination to prevent enteric fever among the soldiers of the British Army. But he achieved greater fame in 1903 by announcing that he had discovered in the blood a substance called opsonin which enabled the white cells or phagocytes of the body to digest germs. This substance was supposed to give the phagocytes the power to devour bacteria, and if the blood contained too little of it or lacked it entirely the phagocytes were unable to do their duty of destroying the germs of the disease and thus keeping the body in good health.

This theory developed the practice of vaccination against all sorts of diseases, including the common cold, to an extent never before known, for Dr. Wright announced that if a sick person had too little opsonin in the blood to vanquish the germs causing the disease, it was possible by taking some of the patient's germs, growing them in the laboratory for a time, then killing them off and injecting a dose of the dead germs under the skin to start the body manufacturing more opsonin to assist the phagocytes to destroy the germs and enable the patient to get well again. More and more doctors who accepted this theory began to treat their patients with injections; a concourse of people who suffered regularly from colds in the winter and the spring sought to protect themselves from these annual nuisances by having a course of injections. In some cases they worked, in other cases they did not, and I recall a careful test made at a school some years ago which proved that injections against colds failed to confer immunity upon the boys.

The opsonic theory of Almroth Wright aroused strong controversy. Numerous workers in various parts of the world carried out clever experiments indicating that the newly-found opsonin was merely the substance which Paul Ehrlich called complement. Metchnikoff, who discovered the wonderful way in which the white cells acted as scavengers of the body and destroyed the germs of disease, named it cytase. Metchnikoff asserted that the white cells themselves manufactured this substance and deposited it in the blood, while Wright held that it was something manufactured in the blood to help the white cells. The controversy persisted for many years before it gradually died out.

But in the days when Fleming was a student it held full sway and it was natural that the young Scotsman should come under the influence of Almroth Wright whose work aroused so much attention. Wright on his part soon recognized the unusual ability of Fleming and it was not surprising that directly the Scottish doctor took his degree he turned his attention to bacteriology.

"Did you have any strong leanings towards bacteriology?" I asked.

"No. I drifted into it, and as I liked it, I stayed in it", the scientist answered quietly.

Thus it was that he began in 1906 to assist Sir Almroth Wright in the inoculation department of St. Mary's Hospital, culturing germs, making vaccines and testing the blood of patients to find out their opsonic index, otherwise how much opsonin their blood contained. The test was delicate, requiring not only care, but much ability and Dr. Fleming soon became adept.

The test was designed to estimate the chances of the patient's recovery by finding out how many germs the white cells, or leucocytes, of a patient could consume. If the white cells were sluggish and not consuming the invading germs with avidity, as virile white cells should, then the doctor could resort to vaccination to restore the normal activity of the white cells to enable them to overcome the germs causing the illness.

Think for a moment exactly what this meant. The blood of a man is seemingly a simple red fluid, yet actually it is most complex, full of magical substances that help the man to survive. Among these mysterious substances are agglutinins which have the power of altering the shape of germs and collecting them into clumps; there are bacteriolysins which have the power of lysing, otherwise dissolving, germs; there are bacteriocidins which have the power of killing germs, but not of dissolving them; there is complement also known as alexine and cytase—to form the link between a white cell and another substance known as amboceptor—the latter having the power to seize a germ with one hand, so to speak, and then seize complement with the other and hold the germ until complement attaches itself to a white cell which destroys the germ.

The blood of a sick man treated at St. Mary's Hospital contained not only these things, but also this invisible substance called opsonin, as well as millions of invisible white cells along with myriads of red cells which gave the blood its red colour and another substance called haemolysin which could rupture the envelopes of the red cells and enable the red fluid inside the cells to pour out like red wine from a bottle. Yet by taking a few drops of blood from a sick man and a few drops from a healthy man Fleming was able by a complicated process to separate the red cells from the white cells and find out how many germs the sick man's white cells could devour and how many germs the healthy man's white cells could engulf. The final stage in this test was the microscope stage on which the scientist placed his slides to count the germs that could be detected in a hundred white cells and it was then a simple matter by comparing the result from the two slides to learn whether the patient's leucocytes were doing their duty or not. Innumerable were the times that Fleming carried out this test when the opsonic theory of Sir Almroth Wright held sway.

Then the medical world was stirred by Paul Ehrlich's discovery of salvarsan, better known as 606, a wonderful chemotherapeutic substance which had an affinity for the spirochaetes which cause the sexual plague of syphilis, and Dr. Fleming experimented with the new drug and, in his own words, "played with the Wasserman reaction", a most intricate test which, if properly carried out, proved whether the person whose blood was being tested was suffering from the disease. It needed acute observation and skill in manipulation, and Fleming with growing experience developed a technical skill that was unsurpassed.

Every day specimens came from the patients in the ward to the little laboratory by the lift well. "What is this?" asked one doctor. "What is that?" asked another. And Fleming, juggling with his agar and bouillon and platinum loop and test tubes and incubators and bunsen burners and stains and microscope slides and Petri dishes, found the germ that was the cause of the trouble.

Day after day and year after year Fleming went to the hospital and climbed the stairs to the little room in the corner of the old building, waging his endless war on disease with test tube and all the other accessories of the laboratory. At the outbreak of the great war of 1914-1918 he reluctantly resigned from the London Scottish to

don uniform and go to France as a captain in the Royal Army
Medical Corps to work in a laboratory which Sir Almroth Wright
set up in the Casino at Boulogne to deal with some of the medical
problems arising out of the war. For a brief period he was obliged
to return to assist in the work at St. Mary's Hospital, then he went
back again to Boulogne to lend his aid to Sir Almroth Wright whose
intensive studies of war wounds led to the hypertonic salt treatment
in which the wounds were continually irrigated by a flow of salt
water which helped to keep them clean and promote more rapid
healing.

With the end of the war in 1918, Fleming returned to the routine
work at St. Mary's Hospital in Paddington, culturing germs,
making vaccines, experimenting and lecturing in the medical school.
In 1922 something unusual on a culture plate led to his first notable
discovery of Lysozyme. And during his investigations his mind was
attracted to the wonder of the eye which looks out upon the world
in an atmosphere laden with myriads of bacteria that float about and
fall on everything. The eye with its moist surfaces acts as a trap for
countless germs, yet nature in her wisdom has made the most
marvellous provision for keeping the windows of the soul clean and
sparkling. The eyelids, moving up and down at intervals—rather
like the wiper of a motor-car screen on a wet day—remove anything
that tends to blur the vision; they lave the magic lenses of the eye
with a fluid which flows automatically from the tear ducts. What is
this fluid? Was there anything unusual in it?

Something prompted Fleming to take a drop of the fluid from a
tear, the human tear which wells to the eye in joy and sorrow.
Juggling with his test tubes and germs he found that the tear which
melts the heart to pity also possessed the remarkable power of
melting germs. Being a scientist who thought in scientific terms
which tend to fog the lay mind, he said there was something in the
tear which lysed the germs; but the average man would have said
that the germs were dissolved. Fleming called the substance
Lysozyme and continued his experiments with other body fluids,
such as saliva, which he found also contained lysozyme. Eventually
he discovered that the white or albumin of an ordinary new-laid
egg was rich in this remarkable substance which had the power of
dissolving bacteria.

Unfortunately his discovery, interesting as it was scientifically,
was of no benefit to the human race. It was a tragic disappointment.
For although lysozyme was able to dissolve germs with great

rapidity, the germs it acted upon were not harmful to man. They were, in the words of science, non-pathogenic, while the germs which caused disease were pathogenic.

It was my privilege to watch Fleming demonstrate the action of lysozyme in his laboratory. On his bench was a small hot water sterilizer and in a box beside it were two sterile test tubes plugged with cotton wool along with a phial of lysozyme and a phial of germs. Taking a test tube in his left hand and deftly withdrawing the plug of cotton wool between his middle fingers, in which he held it securely, he poured into it some warm distilled water. Then he took a platinum loopful of the germs and, tilting the test tube a little to make the water run up the side, inserted the platinum wire and rubbed the germs round and round on the moistened glass just above the level of the water to make sure there were no clots before he swirled the distilled water round in the tube to mix it with the germs. When the mixture was complete he transferred one half of it to the other tube and replaced the cotton wool plugs. Taking the phial of lysozyme, he nicked it with a file and broke off the point, which he drew out in a bunsen flame to extreme fineness before allowing two drops of the lysozyme to fall into one of the test tubes. Both tubes were now clouded with germs and resembled highly-diluted milk. Putting them into the hot water bath for a few seconds, he withdrew them, and as I watched I saw the tube containing the lysozyme grow as clear as crystal while the other remained cloudy. In those few seconds the germs were completely dissolved. It was a beautiful experiment, most dramatic.

During this work on lysozyme he thought out a new method of testing it on several different germs at the same time to see if it destroyed them. It was a simple method which was called the agar cup method. Pouring his agar or other medium to a certain depth into a Petri dish and allowing it to set, he then sowed it with the germ he desired to test and lodged the dish in the incubator for twenty-four hours to start up a good growth of germs. Then with a cork borer he punched out of the gelatine several discs which he removed with the point of a knife. In the circular depressions that were left he poured some of the medium mixed with lysozyme. If the germs grew over this circular patch of lysozyme mixture it was obvious that the lysozyme had no effect on the germs, and if they did not grow over the lysozyme it was equally obvious that the stuff was active against the germs and could stop them from growing, otherwise it could inhibit them.

Did the scientist who discovered lysozyme ever wonder if it would be possible to discover something that would have a similar effect on pathogenic germs? I do not know. But it was rather significant that after experimenting with lysozyme for two years he began to experiment with one antiseptic after another, finding out what they would do and what they would not do. Never did he test one in those days that justified the claims made for it. Most of them, if they killed off pathogenic germs, were toxic to the body cells and a man cannot take something to kill the germs inside him if it is going to destroy the cells of his body. That is the rule of medicine.

So he continued his experiments during such time as he was not lecturing to the students in the medical school to pass on some of his wide knowledge. He was now married and the father of a baby son. Every morning he drove in his car from his house in Chelsea to the hospital where he usually arrived about 10 o'clock; and every evening he drove quietly home for dinner, taking a look at his sleeping son, of whom he was very proud, before sitting down to his meal. In the evening some friends might call in for a game of bridge, or he would drop in at the Chelsea Arts Club of which he was an honorary member. His interests were not entirely confined to science, for he liked sometimes to dabble with oil colours on canvas and at least one of his pictures—of a cow with a barn in the background—found its way into an exhibition. He also had a liking for photography or a game of golf. But these things were merely hobbies which provided relief from his work; they took his mind off it and enabled him to go back to it fresh in the morning.

There was a time in 1926 when a Danish scientist named Moellegaard announced the discovery of a new treatment called sanocrysin, known as the gold treatment for tuberculosis. It aroused great interest owing to the claims that were made for it, and while many doctors were anxious to test it on their patients, many a scientist was just as anxious to carry out experiments with it in the laboratory. Sanocrysin was composed of the metal salts of gold and was administered by injection.

For a time hopes were high that the Danish scientist had discovered a new chemotherapeutic substance that would kill the bacillus of tuberculosis as surely as salvarsan destroyed the parasite of syphilis. Then Sir Almroth Wright, making a culture of the tubercle bacilli, added to the medium as much sanocrysin in proportion as the doctor dare give to a patient. The tubercle bacilli grew unchecked. More and more sanocrysin was added to the medium until Sir Almroth Wright reached a dose twenty times as large as that which a doctor dared to give his patient, but the deadly bacilli continued to thrive, proving, as the famous bacteriologist stated, that "the drug as administered does not exert any noxious effect on the bacillus."

Experience in those days of 1926 had already shown that sanocrysin in the form then available had a serious effect on the kidneys, unless the dose was most carefully adjusted and administered, and now Sir Almroth Wright stated that it had no effect on the bacillus. He showed that the bacillus grew in plasma and blood containing the equivalent of the largest doses that could be given to man, moreover that it flourished as much on these media as on normal plasma and blood. To make sure, he took samples of the blood of patients before giving them a dose of sanocrysin and other samples of the blood after the drug was administered and found that the bacillus grew equally well in both samples.

Meanwhile Fleming carried out experiments with the drug to find out what effect it had on the white cells and discovered that the leucocytes acted more efficiently without it than with it. In the words of Sir Almroth Wright "experiments carried out by my colleague and fellow-worker, Dr. A. Fleming, have shown that even a small addition of sanocrysin to blood notably impairs the phagocytic efficacy of the leucocytes."

So, day by day, Fleming added to his experience and knowledge. He took a cottage in the country at Barton Mills in Suffolk to give him a breath of air during the week-ends and, clothed in a pair of flannel trousers and a tweed jacket, amused himself as the fancy took him. At the bottom of the garden was the mill stream on which he often embarked in an old boat with his small son to go fishing for gudgeon with his friend and colleague Dr. E. W. Todd who shared the little laboratory in St. Mary's Hospital. When Fleming hooked a fish, it must have brought to mind many a happy day spent as a boy fishing for trout in the stream on his father's farm in Ayrshire. At other times the scientist would take his brushes to paint a picture, or a saw to cut up logs in the barn. He liked to pay the most charming of compliments to his friends by planting bulbs in the grassy bank of the stream in the autumn to form their initials and when the flowers were blooming he would invite them down for the week-end to find their own initials flowering by the river, much to their delight.

If there was one thing more than another that the scientist delighted in, it was to race the local train in his motor car. Dr. Todd, recalling those days, was inclined to think that Fleming deliberately dawdled before starting for the station to make sure that by the time he got there the train had left. It was a single railway line with antiquated rolling stock and a locomotive whose record-breaking days, if ever they existed, were long past, so the scientist did not worry. He jammed his foot down on the accelerator and raced along the country road at breakneck speed to catch the train at the next station. And he always succeeded, obviously enjoying the exciting rush through the air.

Returning from a week's holiday in September, 1928, he drove off from Chelsea and crossed Hyde Park to Paddington, where he parked his car as usual at the side of the hospital and climbed the two flights of stairs to the laboratory which was so small that he smilingly told me that it had the advantage of enabling him to swing round in his chair and reach anything anywhere, which was more or less true. A slight push on his wheeled chair as he sat at his bench would allow him to swing round and sit at the typewriter on the table before the fireplace; another turn and he could open the incubators at the back of the room to attend to his cultures. This much can be said for the laboratory which saw the inception of penicillin—no space was wasted. Years later I examined the room to find it was used as a bedroom for doctors on night duty—there was just enough space in it for two single beds and little else.

When Fleming arrived on that September morning he found Dr. Todd, who was working on *haemolytic streptococci*, already busy at his bench just inside the door of the laboratory. After greeting each other, Dr. Todd inquired how Fleming had enjoyed his holiday and what the weather was like and then settled down to work again. Fleming himself at the start of his holiday had been culturing staphylococci in the usual shallow glass Petri dishes which are about four inches in diameter. Some of these lay on his bench while others were lodged on the window ledge. Wishing to find out what sort of growth they had made since he went away, he began examining them, glancing at them with an expert eye, casting aside one here and there that had become contaminated by other bacteria which had crept in and were consequently of no further use to him. He was going through those on the window ledge when he picked up one that had a patch of mould about the size of a florin on it. He glanced at it and was about to discard it when something stopped him and made him look at it more closely. His trained eye noted that while the colonies of staphylococci flourished all over the medium, around this mould the staphylococci were in process of being dissolved. He looked again to make sure that he had made no mistake. Then he moved a step or two with the plate in his hand over to Dr. Todd. "Now look at this—this is very interesting", he said. "I like this sort of thing—it might be important."

Dr. Todd looked at the plate. "Yes, very interesting," he agreed and handed the plate back to Dr. Fleming. To tell the truth, Dr. Todd was not very impressed. "I thought it was something like lysozyme," he told me.

"I think I'll culture it and get a filtrate to see if it will kill staphs or not," Fleming told his colleague and at once made preparations for culturing the bluish-green mould with the fringe of white around the edges. Taking a little of the medium normally used by bacteriologists for growing moulds, he poured it into a test tube. Then he passed his platinum loop through the bunsen flame and took a few spores from the mould and smeared them over the medium in the tube. The spores grew into a pure culture of the mould and from the test tube he seeded the agar medium in a Petri dish and set it aside in a cupboard for four days, by which time the spores had developed into a considerable colony. Taking his platinum loop, he streaked six different kinds of germs from the edge of the mould to the edge of the Petri dish, these germs were the staphylococcus, the streptococcus, and the bacilli of diphtheria, anthrax, typhoid and coli. The results were too striking to be ignored, for while the last two germs grew right up to the mould, the other four could not grow to within a considerable distance of it.

That was the beginning of penicillin, due to an incredible chance, coupled with the acute observation of Fleming. The incredibility of the chance will be better understood when it is known that there are at least six hundred and fifty species of the moulds classified as *Penicillia* and each species is split up into numerous strains, so there are many thousands of different strains. And the astounding thing is that up to early in 1946 only two or three of the species had proved themselves capable of producing penicillin, consequently the odds were millions to one against the spore of a penicillin-producing strain falling upon Fleming's plate. Another noteworthy thing is that the spore of the mould which floated through the window down on that plate at the moment when Fleming took off the cover to look at the germs was sufficiently potent to produce

enough penicillin to force itself on Fleming's notice. Many of the
other strains, although they are active, produce such small quantities
of penicillin that if they had dropped on the plate they would
probably have had so slight an effect as to escape notice.

The chances against a spore falling in such a spot were thus
enormously great, the chances of it being noticed by anyone who
possessed the specialized knowledge that would enable him to seize
the chance and make the most of it were millions to one against.
The spores of this particular mould were rarely found in a laboratory,
although if plates were to be exposed in the laboratories of St.
Mary's hospital to-day, one or two would probably become infected
with the mould owing to the quantities of it being handled.

Fleming's academic career proved him to be a man of wide
knowledge, and since he had qualified there were few advancements
in medical science and the technique of bacteriology which he had
not studied to add to his knowledge. But while he knew much of
other medical subjects, it was upon bacteriology that he had concentrated. The fungus which he was interested in was one of
thousands of moulds forming a special branch of science in itself
and he accordingly passed it on to the mycologist at St. Mary's
hospital so that it could be identified. This was no easy matter.
Although work on moulds had done much to build up Pasteur's
reputation, the field was so wide that the subject had barely been
touched. The mycologist at the hospital did his best to find out
the strain to which Fleming's mould belonged and after considerable trouble and much searching of the literature he announced
that it was *Penicillium rubrum*, or the red *penicillium*. This was the
name which Fleming gave it in his paper mentioned in the beginning
of the chapter, and it happened to be wrong. But to all the prudence
of his race Fleming had added the excessive care that springs from
an intensive scientific training and he went out of his way to pay
credit to the mycologist, Mr. la Touche, for identifying the mould,
so the responsibility was fairly fixed on the shoulders of the
mycologist.

"I never thought it was rubrum," Fleming told me. "It never was
red—it was always yellow."

A letter which Mr. la Touche wrote to Sir Alexander Fleming on
November 3, 1945, provides all the confirmation that is needed:
"As I know that you accepted this nomenclature against your better
judgment perhaps you will allow me to write to Dr. Herrell stating
what I know to be the truth. I think you will remember that it was

your opinion at the time that the mould was *P. chrysogenum*. I regret very much that at the time I did not make a more thorough investigation and am very sorry indeed to have thus misled you into publishing an incorrect statement in your original paper. I trust that this letter makes it clear, although perhaps rather belatedly, that the responsibility for the mistake is entirely my own. I trust also that this letter makes amends in some degree for whatever annoyance my mistake has caused you and that you will consider yourself at liberty to make use of it as you think fit in order to prove that you were not responsible for misnaming this now truly '*notatum*' mould.''

Moulds were not Fleming's subject, and in the circumstances he accepted the opinion of the specialist. Not until the end of 1932 when he published his paper on Penicillin and Potassium Tellurite did he correct the error, after a member of the staff of the Department of Biochemistry in the London School of Hygiene and Tropical Medicine had correctly named the mould as *Penicillium notatum* and been confirmed in his judgment by Dr. C. Thom, the famous American mycologist, who was consulted on the subject by Professor Harold Raistrick whose valuable contribution to penicillin is dealt with in the next chapter.

As Shakespeare said: "A rose by any other name would smell as sweet." And Fleming's *Penicillium* by any other name would have been no less effective. To find out how effective it was, Fleming devoted all his skill to his researches. He watched the first cultures of the fungus spread out from the edges in ever-widening circles. And, as they spread, the older growths in the centre formed a felted mass which became a blue-green colour. Between the fourth and fifth days he observed a change taking place in the medium which was charged with a vivid yellow colour that the mould produced. Under the microscope Fleming detected the minute spores from which the new growth sprang, and saw the tiny tufts of fibres, not unlike camel hair brushes, which gave the mould its name.

Now he started to find out the best medium on which to grow the mould; it was important to learn what kind of food it liked best, what would supply it with the greatest nourishment so that it could flourish and reach its maximum growth. Fleming brewed broths from various organs such as the heart and pancreas. To one batch of broth he added glucose, a sweet substance, also known as grape sugar, produced by treating starch with sulphuric acid; to another batch he added ordinary sugar; to a third he added lactose, a sweet substance derived from curdled milk by separating the liquid from the solid and evaporating it; to a fourth batch he added mannite, another sweet substance of vegetable origin; and to a fifth batch he added dulcite, yet another sweet substance derived from various plants. Having prepared these media, he sowed them with the spores of the mould and placed some on the bench and some in incubators which were set at different temperatures to find out the right amount of heat which best suited them. He saw after two or three days that they flourished best at a temperature of 68 degrees Fahrenheit, that at blood heat, 98.6 degrees the mould barely grew at all and that in higher temperatures it could not survive, while in temperatures lower than 68 degrees it grew slowly. In about four days the broth on which the mould was growing was turned completely yellow.

Dr. Fleming, anxious to find out whether the mould was effecting any chemical change in the medium, carried out some simple tests. A common way of testing a liquid to find out whether it is acid or alkaline is to moisten a piece of litmus paper which, being chemically treated, turns pink if it is damped with acid and blue if the liquid is alkaline. The test is quickly made and a glance reveals whether the liquid is acid or alkaline; but the litmus paper provides only a general test and does not disclose the degree of acidity or alkalinity of the liquid. In these researches of Fleming, it was essential to know the exact strength of the acidity or alkalinity because of the influence it might have upon further experiments. He had no idea whether the knowledge would be unimportant or important, but he wanted to know so that he could apply the knowledge if necessary. As it happened, it turned out to be of vital importance.

The scientist sometimes works his magic in quite simple ways, although he confuses the ordinary people with as many symbols and letters as were used by the fighting services to conceal and confuse the enemy during the war. We need only recall S.H.A.E.F., or W.A.A.F., or F.I.D.O., or A.S.D.I.C., or B.L.A., or B.A.O.R. and so on until we could almost fill a book with these cryptograms. Many a scientific book is so filled and made unintelligible to the reader of average intelligence Well, the scientist can easily find out how much acid a liquid contains by adding sufficient alkali until the liquid is neither acid nor alkaline. It becomes neutral. Similarly if the liquid is alkaline, he simply adds sufficient acid to make the liquid neutral. By measuring the amount of acid or alkali required, he can find out the strength of the acidity or alkalinity.

To simplify things for themselves the scientists have a scale for measuring acidity or alkalinity. Called the pH scale, it is marked off at intervals from numbers 1 to 13 and right in the middle, at number 7, is the neutral line where a liquid is neither acid nor alkaline. Below 7 the liquid is acid, above 7 it is alkaline. Thus pH 6 would be slightly acid; pH 4 would be much more acid, and pH 1 would be strongly acid; while pH 7.5 would be slightly alkaline, pH 9 would be much more alkaline, and pH 13 would be very alkaline.

Fleming made his tests and found that the broth containing the glucose and ordinary sugar became acid in about four days, but with the other broths he could not trace any acid when the mould had been growing for a week. On the contrary, the longer the mould grew on the other broths, the more alkaline they became, so two more facts were discovered about the behaviour of the mould.

It was as natural for the scientist to wonder if any other mould produced the same sort of substance that he had found in the *Penicillium*, as it was for him to test a few to find out. Culturing five different moulds that did not belong to the *Penicillia* family, he found they did not produce a trace of penicillin. Then warming to the search, he took eight different strains of *Penicillia* and tested them to see how they compared with the mould that had dropped in at the window. One after another yielded no penicillin at all and only one out of the eight was found to produce penicillin. How did he find out? That, again, was simple. He knew that penicillin dissolved staphylococci, so the liquid filtered out from any of the broths which failed to kill staphylococci could not contain penicillin. That was as plain as the new test that he devised to test the penicillin. It was a combination of Garré's test of streaking lines of germs across a plate to find out their effect on each other, and Fleming's test of punching discs out of the medium and filling them with lysozyme to find out whether the germs under test would grow over the lysozyme.

To test the penicillin, he cut a strip of agar out of the plate to form a gutter which he filled with a mixture of the agar and penicillin broth. Then he streaked lines of germs at right angles from this gutter across the plate and put the plates into the incubators to see what would happen. The method was clever and effective. The penicillin diffused out into the agar medium in the same way that it diffused out in the first culture that Fleming detected and he was able to learn from one plate the exact effect of the penicillin on five or six different germs. Germs such as the *Bacillus coli* or the *Bacillus influenzae* grew right up to the gutter and even invaded the gutter itself; but he now confirmed his first experiment, that the staphylococcus, the haemolytic streptococcus, the pneumococcus, and gonococcus and the diphtheria bacillus were destroyed by the penicillin, that they could grow only at the end of the line farthest away from the gutter, which was too far away for the penicillin to reach by soaking through the medium. Here was a discovery of importance. The penicillin could destroy the germs of diphtheria, of pneumonia, of the common sexual disease of gonorrhaea, and the germs like staphylococci and streptococci which plague people with sore throats and boils and sore eyes and barber's rash. Here was reason enough for him to pursue his experiments, more than reason to be hopeful. He had proved that penicillin had a marked effect on some germs and no effect on others, and he had an unfailing method of testing it against the germ which was most sensitive. "Staphylococcus is a very suitable microbe on which to test the broth as it is hardy, lives well in culture, grows rapidly, and is very sensitive to penicillin," he wrote.

He next tested the effects of heat upon penicillin. After heating it for an hour at 133 degrees Fahrenheit, he found it remained just as potent, he pushed up the temperature to 176 degrees Fahrenheit for the same time and could detect no change, he tried boiling it for a few minutes and there was little difference—the effect of the penicillin on the germs seemed to be just as powerful. But when he boiled it for an hour he found that three-quarters of the potency was destroyed. Now he wondered what would happen if the penicillin were steamed under pressure in the autoclave, so he made a test, keeping the penicillin in the autoclave at a temperature of 239 degrees Fahrenheit. It lost its potency. But another test proved it would pass through a Seitz filter, so the substance which destroyed germs was able to filter through the asbestos pads of which the filter was made.

Day by day Fleming learned more about the mould and its product and its effect on germs in varying conditions. A few experiments showed him clearly that the penicillin broth was not injurious to the white cells of the human body, for he mixed up a little with some white cells and found that they carried on as usual. His previous experiments with antiseptics had shown him that even the best of them in those days tended to stop the activity of the white cells and to injure them, but the penicillin broth did no harm. Here was something of vital importance if penicillin was to be used for human treatment. He was convinced it was an antiseptic, a slow-acting

OPPOSITE: *Professor Sir Alexander Fleming, the famous Scottish bacteriologist, who first detected that a mould contaminating one of his cultures was preventing the germs from growing, and who called the broth in which he grew this mould "penicillin". Twelve years later Sir Howard Florey and his team of Oxford scientists isolated and purified penicillin for the use of mankind.*

antiseptic, and he began to wonder what would be its effect on human beings. All his tests had been carried out in the laboratory in glass test tubes that were themselves dead things and not composed of living cells. What would be the effect of the penicillin upon the living organism? He took the first step toward finding out by injecting twenty cubic centimetres of the penicillin broth into the vein of a rabbit and found it had no more effect than a similar quantity of broth without any penicillin; he injected some into a white mouse and once more found it was not injurious at all, that there were no toxic symptoms.

With such favourable evidence and experiments so well advanced, Fleming pondered over the problems of separating the penicillin from its broth. He called in the help of his colleague Mr. Ridley, who evaporated some of the penicillin broth until it was a glutinous mass, all brown and sticky from which the penicillin was drawn out by using absolute, or pure, alcohol. Fleming quite rightly desired to know if it were possible to separate the active substance which destroyed the germs from the broth in which it was deposited. And Mr. Ridley did his best to solve the problem. As mentioned, he found that the penicillin would dissolve in pure alcohol and could thus be extracted from the evaporated mass. But when he tried ether and chloroform he was unable to dissolve the penicillin in these volatile liquids.

This was not very promising, but Fleming cast about to try to find out something fresh about the substance which had such a powerful effect on some germs and no effect on others. Anxious to discover when the mould began to deposit the penicillin in the broth, he learned that it began to give off its magic substance on the fifth day, when it took one drop of penicillin broth in twenty of distilled water to kill off his test germs; next day the penicillin had doubled in strength, on the seventh day it was ten times as strong as on the fifth day, for one drop in 200 was sufficient to kill the test germs, while the following day, the eighth day, saw a tremendous increase in the potency of the penicillin which was more than doubled in the twenty-four hours and needed only one drop in 500 to kill off the test germs. That was its maximum potency. After that, the potency of penicillin lessened day by day until it ceased to exist when the mould reached old age. One thing that attracted his attention was the tendency of the mould to produce tiny yellow droplets of fluid on the matted surface, so one day he took one of these drops to make a test. Much to his surprise he found that one

c—m

OPPOSITE: *Professor H. Raistrick, whose family has lived near Rastrick in Yorkshire for a thousand years, and whose life-work on the chemistry of the moulds has won him world fame. His researches on penicillin bridged the wide gap between the unrealized hopes of Fleming and the glorious success of the Oxford scientists.*

drop in 20,000 was sufficient to kill the test germs, while the broth
in which the mould was growing needed one drop in 800, disclosing
a colossal difference in the strength of the penicillin in the two
fluids.

At last Fleming decided to try some of the penicillin on human
patients with infections that were likely to benefit from penicillin.
"Constant irrigation of large infected surfaces in man was not
accompanied by any toxic symptoms, while irrigation of the human
conjunctiva every hour for a day had no irritant effect," he wrote of
these tests.

Fleming, to whom scientific truth was as the breath of life, stated
in his paper that inhibitory substances had been described in the
cultures of many organisms. In particular he singled out the work of
Emmerich and others who had experimented with pyocyanase. This
product of the *Bacillus pyocyaneus* was effective against the germs of
diphtheria, anthrax, cholera and typhoid, but its potency was so
slight when compared with penicillin that it took thirty-three times
as much pyocyanase as penicillin to prevent the growth of the
diphtheria germ—one drop of penicillin was as effective as thirty-
three drops of pyocyanase.

In the light of later knowledge, Fleming's paper was remarkable,
for he not only covered nearly the whole field, but he realized most
of the problems and made considerable progress towards solving
them. Step by step he described the experiments he had conducted.
His list of germs against which penicillin was effective and ineffective
was fairly comprehensive and later workers made few additions.
He stated in the ten points of his summary: "Penicillin is non-toxic
to animals in enormous doses and is non-irritant. It does not interfere
with leucocytic function to a greater degree than does ordinary broth.
It is suggested that it may be an efficient antiseptic for application
to, or injection into, areas infected with penicillin-sensitive
microbes."

That forecast by Fleming was absolutely accurate, yet he found it
impossible of achievement and as late as 1940 he considered the
production of penicillin was impracticable. When the gods of
chance sent that invisible spore floating down to him, he had the
keen observation to seize the chance and the outstanding scientific
ability to develop it almost to the threshold of success. But he was
denied the high honour of giving to the world the penicillin
treatment that we know to-day.

He classed penicillin as an antiseptic. It was much more than that.

It was one of those magic chemotherapeutic substances for which scientists have been seeking ever since Ehrlich discovered salvarsan. Quinine is one of the oldest of these substances.

His paper proved that success was almost in his hand. Why did it escape him? One reason was because penicillin was so unstable. It was what the chemist terms labile. If some penicillin of high potency were placed upon the bench while a little was withdrawn for testing, it was as likely as not that by the time the test was finished the stock of penicillin had lost its potency. In one test the penicillin would play havoc with the germs and next day all the magic was gone from it. The germs of the air, falling into the filtered liquid, were able to destroy the penicillin as easily as a pin pricks a balloon. That was one of the difficulties which Raistrick discovered. Even if the scientist did everything possible to prevent contamination by airborne germs, he found that the power of penicillin disappeared after about ten days or more.

Another thing was that the broth on which the mould was grown gradually became alkaline as the age of the mould increased, and although the mould was depositing penicillin it was also creating this alkalinity which possessed the power of destroying the penicillin. How was it possible to prevent the alkali, which was being produced at the same time in the same fluid as the penicillin, from destroying the penicillin? Fleming solved this problem in a logical way. He added to the broth sufficient acid to neutralize the destructive alkali and a drop over to make the broth ever so slightly acid, just the faintest trace, and found that it rendered the penicillin more stable. With heat destroying it, bacteria destroying it, alkali destroying it, the instability of the substance made it very difficult, if not impossible to work with. How could a man deal with a substance which vanished in thin air in the most uncanny way? The problems were not easily resolved. The difficulty of dealing with this unstable substance cannot be overstated.

Yet this was not all. Asked why he had failed to give the world penicillin after being so near success, Sir Alexander Fleming summed up very simply. "The final stages could be worked out only by the biochemist," he said. "I am a bacteriologist, not a chemist. And we had no chemist attached to the staff of St. Mary's Hospital, so it was impossible for me to carry the work farther."

That Fleming himself realized the importance of his discovery was confirmed by Dr. E. W. Todd, to whom I am indebted for describing what happened when Fleming observed the original plate which laid the foundation of the work. There is also little doubt that Fleming's enthusiasm over his discovery was by no means shared by other members of the staff. "People got a bit tired of him talking about it. They thought he was overstressing it, riding a hobby horse to death," Dr. Todd told me.

In the light of this, it is rather astonishing that Fleming accomplished so much. He was like a prospector who had struck payable ore and had recovered some fine samples for assay. He had located a mine which his utmost efforts could not enable him to work. He felt sure the gold was there, he had found rich samples of it, but the great mass of noble metal lay just beyond his grasp.

For years after the publication of Fleming's paper, penicillin was used in the laboratories of St. Mary's Hospital and other laboratories on the routine tasks of isolating the influenza bacillus and other microbes. Fleming found it of great value in enabling the whooping cough germ to be cultured in a pure state, thus making it possible to prepare a vaccine to prevent this disease. And for years in the laboratories of St. Mary's Hospital, the Lister Institute and elsewhere the strains of the original mould which had flown in at Fleming's window were kept alive, while the human race suffered and died oblivious of the great boon of penicillin which lay hidden in the humble mould.

CHAPTER III

THE MOULD KEEPS ITS SECRET

ALTHOUGH Dr. Fleming was a Scot, with all the pertinacity of his race, he had reached a stage in his experiments beyond which he could make no progress. The instability of penicillin was in itself a formidable obstacle that threatened to defeat all efforts to overcome it. One by one he had forged the first strong links in a scientific chain and had ascertained facts that were proven beyond dispute. In the past few months he had accomplished as much as any bacteriologist could ever hope to perform. The final stages of the work, the separation of penicillin from the broth and its purification, were problems of a highly technical nature that only the trained chemist could solve—and there was no chemist at St. Mary's Hospital with whom he could work. What was he to do?

He did not delude himself. He saw clearly that he was up against a blank wall. Yet he was not content to let matters rest where they were. His interest in penicillin remained so strong that he set in train some further experiments, the results of which were published in the *Journal of Pathology and Bacteriology* in October, 1932, describing how penicillin and potassium tellurite could be used for the selective growth of certain microbes; he showed how the two substances were complementary to each other, inasmuch as the microbes unaffected by penicillin were affected by potassium tellurite, therefore a wide range of microbes could be covered. It may be mentioned that the bacteriologist largely relies on certain dyes to stain his microbes so that he can identify and examine them under the microscope. Some germs stain easily. Others are difficult to stain. One of the commonest dyes is Gram's stain which acts upon certain germs and not on others, and the germs it acts upon are known as Gram-positive because the dye stains them, and the others are known as Gram-negative, because the dye will not colour them. Fleming found in the main that penicillin was potent to the Gram-positive microbes, while potassium tellurite was potent to the Gram-negative microbes and he blended the two substances and used them in what appeared to be a magical way to kill off unwanted microbes and let the selected microbes flourish, as he demonstrated by clever experiments, illustrated with striking plates.

But of greater interest in the light of our present knowledge was his account of penicillin as a dressing for septic wounds: "In penicillin we have a perfectly innocuous fluid which is capable of inhibiting the growth of the pyogenic cocci in dilutions up to 1 in 800. It has been used on a number of indolent septic wounds and has certainly appeared to be superior to dressings containing potent chemicals. It is unlikely that it acts by killing the bacteria directly. Gratia (1923) and others have shown that when compresses of broth are applied to the skin there is an aggregation of phagocytic cells in the deeper layers and he has thus explained the rationale of Besredka's antivirus treatment. Penicillin might then act in the same way as antivirus but superior to ordinary antivirus in that it inhibits the growth of not only one but all the pyogenic cocci. The practical difficulty in the use of penicillin for dressings of septic wounds is the amount of trouble necessary for its preparation and the difficulty of maintaining its potency for more than a few weeks."

Here was evidence of Fleming's efforts to use penicillin for the treatment of wounds; nor did he fail to point out the difficulties of making the penicillin and keeping it.

Meanwhile, in the autumn of 1931, the very chemical problems which baffled Fleming attracted the attention of Professor Harold Raistrick, the Head of the Department of Biochemistry in the London School of Hygiene and Tropical Medicine, that fine building of research and learning that was built through the generosity of the Rockefeller Foundation. Raistrick's one aim in life was to serve science. Tall, well-built, with black hair and dark eyes, he possessed a probity and determination that were typical of the West Riding of Yorkshire where his family had dwelt within reach of the village of Rastrick for a thousand years. Nor could the disappointments of a workaday world destroy his ideals. He was a scientist who sought the truth in everything he did.

Born in Yorkshire at Pudsey, where in his early days he played cricket on the village green with some famous Yorkshire cricketers, Raistrick went to school at the Central High School in the nearby city of Leeds before studying chemistry and gaining his D.Sc. in Leeds University. From Leeds he went on to Cambridge University where he worked in the laboratory of Sir Gowland Hopkins who was then a member of the Medical Research Committee, which later became the present Medical Research Council.

Sir Gowland Hopkins, having watched the science of bacteriology develop, was uneasy about its future. He was inclined to think that bacteriology had reached the end of its tether, that no further advance was possible along the lines then being pursued, so, seeing another possibility, he suggested one day that Raistrick should study the chemistry of pathogenic organisms. The pathogenic organisms as we know are the microbes which cause the ills of suffering humanity and anything new that could be discovered about them might help in the fight against disease. To avoid any confusion of ideas, it will be well to understand that any references in these pages to a chemist, do not mean the chemist who keeps a shop along the street and dispenses pills and cough mixtures, but the scientist who studies the lifeless compounds with a view to finding out the substances of which they are made. The biochemist, on the other hand, is a scientist who has specialized in one particular branch of chemistry. Bio means life, and the biochemist is a man who studies living organisms, animal or vegetable, with the aim of discovering the chemical compounds of which they are composed, with the ultimate object of solving the problem of life itself.

Now Raistrick had adopted biochemistry as his life work and was well fitted to carry out the investigations suggested by Sir Gowland Hopkins. There was, however, one drawback. Raistrick, who was initially interested in the chemistry of the pathogenic organisms, became much more interested indeed in the chemistry of the moulds. Accordingly he began some general researches, but instead of devoting all his attention to the pathogenic organisms with a view to discovering the chemical composition of the germs of disease, he gave more and more time to studying the moulds, or fungi, in an effort to learn about their chemical products. He found little to encourage him, yet he felt it was the work he was called upon to do.

So he came to devote all his attention and talents to the moulds in order to find out their actions and reactions, how they grew and propagated their species, their likes and dislikes in the way of food and how they were affected by heat and cold. No cattle breeder ever studies the idiosyncrasies of his herds to such a degree of intensity as that which Raistrick devoted to the moulds he cultured in his incubators. He was one of the pioneers in a branch of science which the great Pasteur had lighted for a brief spell with his own genius and which had not been developed as it might have been, owing to the greater inherent interest aroused by the germs of disease. The call of science to save human life was so irresistible that the growing army of bacteriologists never lacked recruits, while any young man with scientific leanings who preferred to study the mould growing on a pot of jam in preference to the germs which cause human sickness would have been regarded as rather odd. The public acclamations and support which greeted discoveries in bacteriology were a strong incentive to the development of this science and were no doubt largely responsible for the neglect of the moulds. Occasionally an exceptional man was prepared to devote his life to the chemistry of these lowly fungi without thought of acclamation or reward, but generally the chemistry of the moulds was so neglected as to be almost new when Raistrick started to work on them. It is true that Pasteur pointed the way, but few who came after were sufficiently interested to follow so unpromising a path.

Raistrick did not seek public acclamations. He sought the truth. However unpromising the path looked to others, it was to him the most promising path of all. It led to new fields, full of problems that appealed to him, so he pursued his researches as a member of the research staff of the School of Biochemistry in Cambridge University despite adverse opinions. While he worked on, unknown to the general public, the soundness of his work began to be noted by acute observers and his reputation spread beyond the confines of a select scientific circle into the bigger business sphere.

Thus it came about that after seven years he was induced to discard his academic life at Cambridge to embark on a commercial career. That, at any rate, was how it appeared. But appearances were deceptive and the new life held out far greater opportunities and a wider field for his researches than he had enjoyed at Cambridge. Nobels, the famous manufacturers of explosives who were one of the founder firms of Imperial Chemical Industries, offered him a contract for five years to pursue any researches he liked into any moulds which he cared to select. It was a magnificent tribute to Raistrick. The directors and scientific advisers of this powerful firm were so impressed with his abilities that they were prepared to give his researches all the requisite financial backing and leave him to follow his own lines of investigation without retaining any power to veto anything he might care to do. What more could a scientist want? He was to have a well-equipped laboratory up in Ayrshire with all the money necessary to carry on his work without fear or favour.

No wonder he accepted for, as well as doing the work he loved, there was the prospect of enjoying his favourite sport of fishing for trout in loch and stream or pitting his patience and skill against the wary salmon haunting a lonely pool in the river. Naturally he undertook, in return, to relinquish his claims in any discovery he might make during the term of his engagement. It cannot be too strongly emphasized that Raistrick was a scientist whose overriding aim in life was to discover new chemical substances. Directly he had done that, his work was completed. It was not his duty to solve the problems of finding out whether the substances he discovered were useless or useful, whether they could be exploited commercially or not. These things were quite outside his sphere. With the isolation of a new substance his task was finished. It remained for other men to discover if it was useful and work out processes for its commercial exploitation.

Well, Raistrick quietly pursued his researches in the Nobel laboratories without interference and without being continually harried to produce profitable results. The men who appointed him were wise. They looked ahead. They did not mind waiting two or three years. They trusted in his scientific ability, knowing full well that one discovery might prove to be of incalculable value.

Events justified their judgment, for as time went on he isolated from his despised moulds one chemical after another, chemicals undreamed of by chemists and hitherto unknown to science. Nor was this all, for he did with a German process something that the vaunted German scientists could not do themselves—he wrestled with a very costly and utterly uneconomic laboratory method of making glycerine by fermenting a sugary solution of sodium sulphite with ordinary baker's yeast until he had turned it into a sound economic process.

As most people know, glycerine is a by-product of soap-making, and glycerine with the addition of nitric acid is the basis of explosives. As a result of this work, Nobels became possessed of an entirely new secret process which would enable them to manufacture the glycerine they needed without recourse to the soap manufacturers at all, providing they built the necessary factory and fitted it with plant of a revolutionary design. When everything was worked out, they informed the soap manufacturers of the new process. It must have been a shock to the soap manufacturers. Here was a threat to lose for ever their most important market for their most important by-product. The soap manufacturers, being keen business men, promptly reduced the price of glycerine so that it was more profitable for the explosive manufacturers to continue to purchase their glycerine from the usual sources than to go to the capital expenditure of

building an immense factory in which they could have manufactured
all the glycerine they needed. There was consequently no necessity
to exploit Raistrick's new discovery. His revolutionary process of
making glycerine remained unused, ready to be put into operation
if ever the necessity arose.

In 1929, the same year that Fleming published his first paper on
penicillin, a new Department of Biochemistry was created in the
London School of Hygiene and Tropical Medicine in the University
of London and Raistrick was honoured by being offered the chair.
This was a great tribute to him and his work. Already he had isolated
from moulds sixteen new chemical substances that were entirely
unknown to science. He considered the matter carefully. Every
man in the entire building housing the Biochemistry Department
was a qualified medical man. He was the only man among them
without a medical degree. He was purely a scientist whose knowledge of moulds was unsurpassed in the country, and he was not
prepared to give up his life work, so he offered to accept the Chair of
Biochemistry provided he was permitted to continue his investigations of the moulds. This was agreed, and Raistrick resumed his
academic career and his researches as Professor of Biochemistry in
the University of London.

As the Head of this new department, he had his spurs to win
and a name to make for his school in the world of science and
learning. Before him lay a wide field of investigation in which
he was determined to build up the reputation of the school. There
were so many things for him to work upon, so many promising
moulds with important problems for him and his students to study
that it required a good deal of consideration to make a selection from
the mass of material available. However the work of the school was
planned and the students had settled down to their lectures and
experiments with the keenest interest by the time that Raistrick
made up his mind to undertake the essential chemical researches on
penicillin.

Having decided to investigate the mould, Raistrick reviewed the
position. He was equipped with a wide knowledge and technical
skill that came of long experience, and in Dr. P. W. Clutterbuck
he had a clever young chemist on whom he could rely for the fullest
collaboration in some of the chemical work. But although Fleming
had posed a chemical problem, it could not be resolved without
making tests which demanded the assistance of a trained bacteriologist. Thinking it over, Professor Raistrick went upstairs to the

Bacteriological Department where he had a chat with Professor W. W. C. Topley to see what could be done.

Upon leaving Manchester University to occupy the Chair of Bacteriology in the London School of Hygiene, Professor Topley had taken with him Dr. Reginald Lovell who, before studying bacteriology in Manchester, had passed as a fully qualified veterinary surgeon. Professor Topley broached the subject to Dr. Lovell. "Look here," he said, "Raistrick and Clutterbuck are working on penicillin and they want someone to carry out the bacteriological tests. Would you care to help them?"

"What do they want me to do?" inquired Dr. Lovell, who was experimenting at the time with the mixed bacteria found in the mouth, among which the pneumococcus was prominent.

Professor Topley explained.

"All right," agreed Dr. Lovell, and in this way Professor Raistrick and Dr. P. W. Clutterbuck and Dr. R. Lovell became associated in the second attempt to solve the mystery of penicillin. The fact that Dr. Lovell was already working with the pneumococcus made him use the same germ as the test organism in carrying out his penicillin researches.

Studying Fleming's paper, Raistrick and Clutterbuck duplicated some of the experiments to confirm for themselves what the Scottish scientist had done. This was no reflection on Fleming, but the normal scientific preliminary to any further researches based on his work. Fleming was the pioneer who had started to explore a new realm of science. He had blazed the trail and managed to penetrate for a considerable distance. It was therefore right that the men who proposed to carry on further should follow in his footsteps until they were ready to launch out into the unknown vistas ahead.

Considering the careful way in which Fleming had marked each step, it might have been expected that further progress would have been easy. But it was not. From Fleming's culture of the mould, Raistrick started to grow cultures on a medium similar to that which Fleming found to be most suitable. As we know, it was a nutrient broth made from special organs such as heart muscle and pancreas that took some time to prepare and was expensive to make. The task of growing these cultures was delegated to Miss L. Farrell and Mr. J. H. V. Charles, the mycologist.

At the same time Professor Raistrick asked the Lister Institute in Chelsea to supply him with one of their cultures of Fleming's organism as well as another culture of *Penicillium chrysogenum* that

was originally discovered by Dr. Thom, the famous American mycologist. It is not generally known that the British nation owns a
national collection of germs and pays for the upkeep of the collection,
just as it pays for the upkeep of the racehorses in the national stud,
so nationalization of germs and horses was achieved long ago. In
the British National Collection of Type Cultures are to be found
specimens or types of most of the microbes that cause human
illnesses as well as many that are harmless. They are card indexed
with details of their origin and other essential facts, as though they
were pedigree cattle, provided with the temperatures which suit
them best, given their favourite food and cultured regularly to
maintain the strength of the strain and prevent the microbes from
dying. There are millions of them living snugly in their test tubes
and multiplying at a prodigious rate. And if any laboratory or
doctor wants a particular microbe for some specific purpose, he
can order it from the British National Collection of Type Cultures
and be sure that the order will be carried out with unfailing accuracy
and the germs dispatched in their test tube as promptly as possible.

So Professor Raistrick received Fleming's *Penicillium* and Thom's
Penicillium from the Lister Institute and started to grow them in
addition to that which he obtained from Dr. Fleming. And as soon
as possible he secured another of the moulds, *Penicillium notatum*
Westling, from Dr. Thom.

It was first discovered in Raistrick's department that Fleming's
mould was wrongly named and that it was in fact *Penicillium notatum*,
and not *P. rubrum*. To make quite sure on the point, Professor
Raistrick sent a culture of Fleming's organism to Dr. Thom in
America who replied: "I have cultivated Fleming's organism under
several different conditions and cannot agree with the nomenclature
as *P. rubrum* either in my sense of my 1910 paper or in the sense of
Biourge's monograph. In fact, I believe this culture, although
showing some divergencies in culture reactions, to be much closer
to *P. notatum* of p. 264 in my book than to the groups discovered on
pp. 249-50 as indicated by the nomenclature used."

Dr. Thom has written what is probably the world's standard
work in English on "The Pencillia" and his book is to be found
in most laboratories. But it would be a mistake to think that he
identified Fleming's mould without trouble. On the contrary the
identification entailed a series of tests which emphasize the multi-
tudinous details of the scientific work involved in solving all the
problems of penicillin. Dr. Thom grew Fleming's mould in his

incubators and found that it was able to digest milk and that it soon turned a solid gelatine into a liquid and produced a vivid yellow pigment. The mould had a sweet tooth. It liked sugar. So long as it had plenty of sugar which it could digest and ferment it maintained a fine blue-green colour; but if it were starved of sugar, it refused to deposit anything but a faint trace of the yellow pigment in the medium.

Thus it came about that researches and experiments took place on both sides of the Atlantic to try to find the right name of Fleming's mould. And even when Dr. Thom had given his opinion, Fleming's mould remained none the less mysterious. Because it produced this vivid yellow colour in the medium, it seemed to belong to the *Penicillium chrysogenum* group of moulds. If this were true, it was obvious that the mould with this name should yield up penicillin into the medium. But when Professor Raistrick handed over some of this penicillin medium for Dr. Lovell to test by Fleming's method against the pneumococcus, the matter was by no means solved, for the germ which would have died if there had been any penicillin in the medium, simply flourished and multiplied, so Raistrick learned that the production of a yellow pigment was not necessarily accompanied by the production of penicillin.

Then he tried another line of investigation. He took the broth on which *Penicillium notatum* Westling had been grown and, having filtered it, asked Dr. Lovell to test it. Again the germs thrived. It was very puzzling. Here was a true *Penicillium notatum*, but it certainly did not produce penicillin.

From the very beginning of his researches Raistrick realized that if penicillin came up to the expectation of Fleming and fulfilled all the hopes engendered by the laboratory experiments, its production on a huge scale for clinical treatment would have been jeopardized by the difficulty of securing enough raw material in the shape of heart muscle, pancreas and other organs to make the millions of gallons of nutrient broth necessary for the growth of the mould. Nor did Raistrick overlook the economic factor of the high cost of Fleming's medium. To make it for laboratory experiments entailed a great deal of time and trouble; to make it on a commercial scale seemed to be impossible. He felt sure of two things. His experimental work would be simplified and hastened if he could manage to grow the mould on some chemical medium—a synthetic medium. And by finding some suitable chemical medium it might eventually be possible to produce penicillin on a commercial scale. So while he was culturing Fleming's mould on nutrient broth, he started to try to grow the mould on a chemical medium. Having already grown other moulds on synthetic media, his previous experience now proved invaluable, so he made up his media, adding sugar and a few common chemicals to this one and glucose and some other common chemicals to that in different proportions. Planting the spores of the mould, he set the flasks in the incubators to see what would happen. His scientific eye could tell at a glance whether the moulds were growing or wilting away as easily as a nurseryman could tell whether his tomatoes and lettuces were flourishing or failing.

One thing was soon defined. It was plain to see that there was a good chance of growing this mould on a chemical medium. And it was equally plain that although the mould could survive on a chemical medium, it grew more slowly than it did on the nutrient broth. Within two months Raistrick had solved the problem of growing the mould on a chemical medium. He had forged a vital link in the scientific chain which made commercial production possible—if penicillin was worth it. His medium prepared by Dr. H. G. Turley was a variation of a well-known medium that was originally prepared by two scientists, Czapek and Dox, so it became known as the modified Czapek-Dox medium.

Raistrick soon prepared for a large-scale experiment which he hoped would do much to solve the problems and mysteries of Fleming's organism. Taking some distilled water, he added the necessary quantities of a few cheap mineral salts such as sodium nitrate, magnesium sulphate, potassium chloride and other chemicals along with some glucose from which the mould could derive the carbon essential to its growth. Clutterbuck made up a hundred litres of this medium as carefully as any doctor's prescription, for it was essential to combine the exact quantity of each chemical to enable the mould to grow freely. Taking a hundred glass flasks of a conical shape that had previously been sterilized to rid them of all germs, Raistrick and Clutterbuck poured into each flask two-fifths of a litre and promptly plugged each flask with cotton wool to exclude atmospheric bacteria. Although every precaution was taken to prevent infection while the medium was being poured into the flasks, it was impossible for Raistrick or anyone else to swear that some air-borne germs had not entered with the fluid, so to make sure that the medium and the flasks were quite germ-free, they steamed for half an hour. The next day and the following day they were steamed again for the same period, by which time any germs which may have entered were certainly destroyed.

Six days previously a large batch of new cultures of Fleming's organism and another batch of *Penicillium chrysogenum* had been prepared. These were sporing nicely by the time the flasks were ready. The flasks were planted generously with the spores of the cultures and well shaken to distribute them before being placed in the incubators where they were allowed to remain for a period ranging from three weeks to a month. This was longer than the time taken by Fleming to grow his moulds on the nutrient broth, but for the moment this did not matter. It was far more important to learn how the moulds reacted to the new synthetic medium during this big experiment. Waiting until they had consumed practically all the sugar, to mark the end of their growth, Raistrick withdrew samples of the medium from the two different moulds and tested them.

Then all the fluid was filtered off from the two batches of mould, the moulds were collected together and squeezed until the last drop of fluid was crushed from them and the scientist was left with just over eight gallons of dark brown liquid that was slightly alkaline. By adding sulphuric acid with the utmost care, he neutralized the alkalinity and gradually made the fluid fairly acid. As he did so the yellow pigment collected and precipitated in flakes which were easily filtered out. But if he poured in the acid too quickly the pigment remained in solution and could not be filtered out at all.

He soon learned that his yellow pigment was not penicillin, and that it contained no penicillin, for all the penicillin escaped through the filter, as was easily proved by testing samples of the fluid and samples of the pigment in the usual way against the test germs. By carrying out a number of chemical tests of a highly technical nature he and Clutterbuck were able to fix the chemical formula for this pigment, which he named chrysogenin. They found out by experiment that this new pigment would dissolve readily in ether as well as in a number of fluids which the chemist uses to dissolve other chemicals. Time and again they tried to crystallize it by evaporating the ether or other solvent, but each time the pigment was deposited on the sides of the vessel like a glaze or coat of varnish.

Testing the pigment by mixing it up with a light petroleum, they found that chrysogenin would not dissolve in the petroleum, so they dissolved some pigment with ether and then added the light petroleum. To Raistrick's satisfaction he saw the pigment precipitate in the form of a light yellow powder that was flour-like and not in crystal form at all. This powder contained an impurity in the form of a reddish-brown matter, so he experimented to try to remove it. This time he solved the problem by discovering that benzene would dissolve the chrysogenin without dissolving the impurities, so it was easy to filter out the impurities. To regain the dissolved chrysogenin from the benzene, he merely added some light petroleum which precipitated the pure pigment in the form of a powder. If this seems simple, the following quotation from the paper of Clutterbuck, Lovell and Raistrick will suggest that their experiments were otherwise:

"Chrysogenin on warming with dilute NaOH gives amongst other unidentified products acetaldehyde and sorbic acid. It does not methylate with ether-diazomethane, but gives with ether-nitrobenzene-diazomethane a monomethyl derivative which no longer gives the characteristic olive-brown colour with $FeCl_3$. The pigment reduces readily with Zn and HCl giving a colourless compound dihydrochrysogenin, $C_{18}H_{24}O_6$ (found: C64.48%; H7.10%; $C_{18}H_{24}O_6$ requires C64.27%; H7.20%) which readily reoxidizes in air, gives a wine-red colour with $FeCl_3$, and with ether-diazomethane gives a dimethyl derivative which shows a green colour with $FeCl_3$. The above facts suggest that chrysogenin contains a quinol nucleus. Investigation of its structure is reserved for a separate communication."

The ways of the biochemist are certainly long and arduous and he uses a technical language which can only be understood by the people when it is translated for them.

One result of Raistrick's experiments was therefore the isolation of a new pigment which he called chrysogenin. A second substance extracted from the fluid of the mould was a protein which he analyzed during a series of difficult tests and split up into eight different forms of nitrogen.

Exercising all his scientific knowledge and skill, he sought to solve the last problems and isolate this elusive penicillin. In well-thought-out experiments he carried the work forward, recording new facts, the importance of which could not at the moment be gauged. He proved that although Fleming's mould took longer to grow on the new chemical medium, it also produced more penicillin. On Fleming's nutrient broth the mould took eight days to reach the peak of its production, whereas on the chemical medium it took from sixteen to twenty days. On the fifteenth day a mixture of one part of penicillin to 640 parts of medium would inhibit the growth of the pneumococcus; the next day the penicillin had doubled in strength and one part in 1,280 of medium stopped the growth of the test germ. Within two days the strength diminished to one in 640 which was maintained until the twenty-second day, when it dropped to one in 160 up to the thirty-first day.

The problem of keeping the filtered fluid in an active state was partly overcome by storing it in an ice chest at 0 degrees centigrade. When stored away the active fluid had a strength of one in 1,280. It dropped on the seventh day to half, or one in 640, which was maintained for three weeks. By the third month it was down to one in 320 which was retained to the end of the fourth month, so in sixteen weeks the potency of the penicillin was reduced to one quarter of its original strength. Despite the loss of potency, it was rather promising to retain any activity at all for so long a period. The bugbear was the ease with which the filtered liquid was infected with bacteria from the air. After two batches of penicillin fluid had been contaminated in carrying out storage experiments in the ice chest, Raistrick decided to seek other means of storage. So he slightly acidified samples of the fluid, filtered them through a sterilized Seitz filter into sterile flasks and stored them in the refrigerator at 0 degrees centigrade. By this method he found that he could keep the fluid for three months without any loss of activity at all. This was a big step forward. He made the fluid slightly acid before storing it, and to test it on the sensitive germs he neutralized this acidity by giving the fluid the faintest trace of alkalinity.

Then he faced the problem of concentrating the fluid while preserving its penicillin content. Obviously any treatment would be complicated, if not made impossible, by the necessity of handling gallons of fluid of which only a minute percentage was useful, therefore he tried evaporation. Making the penicillin fluid slightly acid, he exhausted all the air from the flask to create a vacuum and then subjected it to a heat of 104 to 113 degrees Fahrenheit until the fluid had diminished to one fifth of its original volume. This diminished quantity was much easier to handle, but a test disclosed that the active penicillin had disappeared. So he tried again. This time he made the fluid slightly alkaline. The result was not encouraging. Before the fluid was evaporated it took one part in 1,280 to stop the pneumococcus from growing, and after evaporation the activity had diminished to one-sixteenth of its original power.

This great loss of activity was too wasteful to contemplate, so Raistrick tried for a third time. He was lucky. He found that if he acidified the fluid slightly so as to bring it between 5 and 6 on the pH scale the penicillin was more stabilized and did not lose more than half of its activity. So by trial and error Raistrick and Clutterbuck worked out a method whereby the yellow pigment, chrysogenin, and the proteins could be filtered out of the medium by acidifying it to a certain degree, and then by decreasing the acidity it could be evaporated with a great part of its penicillin content intact.

Then Raistrick faced up squarely to the main problem of getting rid of all the superfluous fluid and isolating the penicillin itself. Fleming had tried to extract the penicillin by mixing the fluid with ether, in the hope that the penicillin would dissolve in the ether which, being very volatile, would quickly evaporate and leave him with the pure penicillin. But although Fleming tried hard to accomplish this, he failed and stated that penicillin could not be extracted by ether.

Raistrick, who was familiar with the miraculous changes that could be brought about by adding a little more of this chemical or a spot less of that to a fluid, was not so sure. He carried out a series of experiments to try to extract the penicillin with ether, and I quote the following summary from his paper in the *Biochemical Journal*:

"From the above experiments it appears that the antibacterial substance is not identical with either chrysogenin or the protein, and that the greater part of these substances can be removed by suitable adjustment of the pH and filtering without serious loss of antibacterial activity. The antibacterial substance is extremely labile, becoming inactivated during evaporation of an ether solution in a stream of air and by evaporation *in vacuo* at 40-45 degrees in both fairly acid and alkaline solutions. It is, however, more stable at pH 5-6 and may be extracted with ether from acid solution."

Fleming had learned that as the mould increased in age, the medium on which it grew increased in alkalinity and Fleming's broth was therefore much too alkaline to allow the penicillin to be extracted with ether.

Thus Raistrick opened a way which Fleming thought was barred, and the biochemist succeeded, with difficulty, in creating a method whereby the penicillin could be extracted in ether. He now had a concentrated solution of ether and medium consisting of one-fifth of the original quantity and he was hopeful that by evaporating the ether in a current of air he would be left with a highly concentrated penicillin. So he blew the ether away under a blast of sterilized air and expected to find the penicillin in the residue.

It was not there. It had vanished. Not a trace of activity could be found. He had never met with such a thing in chemistry before. It was as much of a miracle as it would have been if a child had opened his mouth and swallowed St. Paul's Cathedral in the sight of a million Londoners and toddled off without showing any internal disturbance or increase in girth.

Raistrick was puzzled. The nearer he got to penicillin, the more it was veiled in mystery. As a scientist he had been taught to believe in the indestructibility of matter, yet here was an experiment which seemed to indicate that some substance, the existence of which had been proved, might indeed disappear. It was an extraordinary chemical phenomenon.

Pondering over the problem, he decided to try another experiment. This time he added some distilled water, amounting to one-fifth of the original volume of the combined medium and ether, to the ethereal extract and then evaporated the mixture in a vacuum at the usual temperature. The addition of water changed the solution from a concentrated ether solution into a watery solution, and as the ether evaporated it left the penicillin behind in the water. When Professor Raistrick came to test his solution he found that it was still active, that it contained penicillin with a quarter of the activity of the original fluid. It was another obstacle overcome, another step forward. But the penicillin was still in solution and the problem of isolating it in a dry form remained to be solved.

When I discussed with Sir Alexander Fleming the reason for his own failure to complete his work after having achieved so much, he answered frankly that it was because there was no chemist attached to St. Mary's Hospital to do the chemical work. When I confessed that I was just as puzzled to find that Professor Raistrick had discontinued his experiments when he had penicillin practically in his grasp, Fleming mentioned that it was because Raistrick had no bacteriologist to work with him.

As Raistrick was averse to discussing the matter, I pursued inquiries elsewhere and at length confirmed that it was the simple truth.

While the work was going on at the end of 1931, Clutterbuck and Lovell wrote a brief note on it for the *Journal of the Society of Chemical Industry—Transactions* in which they mentioned that

Fleming's mould gave chiefly penicillin and that a method of isolation of a crude but highly active preparation had been evolved. The following autumn at the very moment when Clutterbuck and Lovell were correcting their parts of the joint paper for the *Biochemical Journal* a knock came on the door. Clutterbuck rose and went outside. He returned a few moments later looking so white and shaken that it was impossible to hide his distress.

"What's wrong?" Lovell exclaimed.

"Charles is dead. He's been killed by a bus," was the response.

It was a sad end for the gifted mycologist who had proved so helpful in these penicillin researches.

In their paper, Clutterbuck, Lovell and Raistrick stated: "The investigation of the isolation and chemical nature of penicillin is being continued."

That intention, however, was nullified, because during the same autumn of 1932 Dr. Lovell resigned his appointment in the Department of Bacteriology at the London School of Hygiene to join the staff of the Royal Veterinary College, a move which deprived Professor Raistrick of the help of the bacteriologist. Without bacteriological tests, the biochemist was unable to continue, because he could not tell whether his solutions were active or inactive, whether they contained penicillin or not.

With the resignation of Dr. Lovell and the publication of the results of the penicillin researches in the *Biochemical Journal*, the interest in Raistrick's work died down. Had he been encouraged at that time to carry on his work, and had a bacteriologist been forthcoming to perform the necessary tests, it is possible that the world might have been given penicillin ten years earlier.

As it was, Fleming, the bacteriologist, had failed for lack of a chemist in his team; and Raistrick, the biochemist, was obliged to cease work for lack of a bacteriologist to test the penicillin he produced.

Nevertheless Raistrick's work was good. He had isolated a new pigment and a protein from the medium. Were these important links in the scientific chain? They may be termed negative links. They proved that chrysogenin, the new pigment, was not penicillin and that the protein was not penicillin. The positive links were more numerous. They were, that penicillin was destroyed by excess acid and excess alkali as well as by bacterial contamination; that penicillin could be separated out of the medium by ether; that penicillin could be stored in the ice chest at a low temperature for three months without complete loss of activity. And above all that the mould could be grown upon a synthetic medium. The last was important, for it was a big step towards economic production if penicillin proved to be of value. And Raistrick's method of extracting the penicillin from the medium by ether was one of the vital links which enabled the Oxford team years later to forge the final links in the chain.

In the end Raistrick was faced like Fleming with the fact that penicillin was extremely unstable. It was here to-day and gone to-morrow, so unreliable that its existence could never quite be counted upon, because it could be so easily destroyed.

Fleming stated that penicillin could not be extracted with ether. But Raistrick had shown how this was possible. He and Clutterbuck reached the climax of their work to receive a shock as shattering to them as the atomic bomb was to the Japanese.

"We had found out that penicillin was extremely labile and that its potency was destroyed by both acid and alkali and that when we extracted it with ether it disappeared. Such a thing was never known to a chemist before", Raistrick said. "It was unbelievable. We could do nothing in the face of it, so we dropped it and went on with our other investigations and experiments."

Two years later Professor Raistrick's brilliant work on moulds was recognised by his election as a Fellow of the Royal Society, the highest honour which Science could bestow upon him. He became known as the Founder of Mould Chemistry and he and his staff succeeded in isolating a hundred entirely new chemicals from these lowly fungi which have for so long been regarded as curses of mankind and may turn out to be some of mankind's greatest blessings. Arranged in one case alone I saw forty-eight new chemical substances in the form of crystals in little glass tubes. Some were red, others orange, light yellow and dark yellow, blue and brown and white and buff—what useful purpose they may serve is at present unknown, but some of them would seem to have a future as dyes and perhaps others may serve in medicine or in industry. The work of Professor Raistrick on the moulds was so outstanding that the Royal Society marked it by publishing a volume devoted entirely to his papers.

Difficult as it may be for the average person to think that the patch of mould on top of a pot of blackcurrant jam is worthy of any scientific study at all, it would be even more difficult to imagine the endless variety and colour that the moulds assume. One afternoon in the Biochemistry Department of the London School of Hygiene, I met the mycologist, Mr. G. Smith, M.Sc., F.R.I.C., who showed me the biggest and most varied collection of moulds I have ever seen, numbering some three thousand. At one time Professor Raistrick and Mr. Smith were troubled by the contamination of one mould by another. A pure sub-culture of a mould would be made and the test tube plugged with the usual plug of sterilized cotton wool. For a while the mould would flourish. Then one day Mr. Smith would find a new mould starting to grow, a mould quite different from the original culture. Theoretically the thing was not possible. The culture tubes were plugged with cotton wool through which no spores could make their way, yet somehow new spores were being introduced into the tubes while the tubes remained undisturbed by human hands. In the beginning the tubes were sterile, the medium was sterile, the cotton-wool plugs were sterile and the mould was a pure culture. It was as though a jeweller went to a sealed safe and found upon opening it that some diamonds and rubies had been placed inside while the safe remained sealed and unopened. Impossible as this seems, so far as the culture tubes were concerned, Mr. Smith had the contaminated moulds to prove that it was possible.

He soon found the explanation. It was a mite so small as to be invisible to the naked eye. This pest burrowed its way down through the plug of cotton wool until it broke through the barrier and could reach the mould which it contaminated with the spores of other moulds, collected among the microscopic hairs of its legs and body while crawling about the outside world.

The best way of dealing with the pest was soon discovered. It was to keep the moulds in a refrigerator where the low temperature prevented the mites from breeding and slowed down their respiration until they died. The method was most effective, and the collection of moulds was thenceforward safely housed in test tubes packed in zinc wire boxes on the shelves of a refrigerator. The moulds were like Joseph's coat of many colours, ranging through various shades of white, cream, yellow, pink, red, green, blue, grey and purple to a jet black. Here as clumps and colonies and hairy felts they survived on the various media despite the low temperature. Each culture tube was plugged with cotton wool of a distinct colour, it might be pink or blue or green, to indicate at a glance the medium on which the mould was being grown. The method of marking was necessary because the mould during its growth so changed the colour of the medium that even the trained mycologist could not recognise it.

These moulds had their records as though they were pedigree bulls, and every six months each mould was sub-cultured to give it a new lease of life and prevent it from dying out. And from time to time the medium was changed to allow the moulds a different diet, otherwise to vary their vitamins. From these moulds any number of sub-cultures could be made for growing the moulds on a big scale in the culture room where the temperature was automatically controlled and the walls were honeycombed with shelves carrying hundreds of conical flasks. A man of vision and knowledge could say with truth that any one of these moulds in the little culture tubes might prove to be the foundation of a gigantic industry employing thousands of workers.

Here is Professor Raistrick's own account of his final attempt to isolate penicillin: "On extraction of the acidified liquid of *Penicillium notatum* with ether, we placed the ether solution in a little glass dish and left it on the bench all night. By next day the ether had evaporated and we found at the bottom of the glass a yellowish-brown glaze resembling varnish. It was a most intractable substance that gave me no indication that it would ever crystallize. But there is no doubt that it was a very crude, but concentrated, film of penicillin, probably as strong as the first concentration of penicillin obtained by the Oxford team."

That treacly film in the little glass jar which defied all the efforts of Raistrick and Clutterbuck to crystallize it marked the end of the second attempt to find the elusive penicillin. If the two biochemists had not been so baffled by the inexplicable disappearance of the penicillin after the ether was evaporated and if Dr. Lovell had remained on Professor Topley's staff to co-operate with them for another year, the world might have been granted the boon of penicillin in 1933.

Although Clutterbuck and Lovell and Raistrick were so close to success, I did not realize the true position until I had travelled to one of the loveliest reaches of the Thames to see Dr. R. Lovell who was then the Deputy Director of the Research Institute in Animal Pathology of the Royal Veterinary College. We were discussing the earlier work on penicillin when Dr. Lovell remarked: "I remember making a note in my card index to try penicillin on mice infected with pneumococcus."

Instantly I saw the wonderful chance that Dr. Lovell had allowed to pass, for this was a mouse experiment similar to that which gave Florey the first proof of the efficacy of penicillin. "Do you think you could find those references?" I asked, for I was anxious to confirm the evidence.

"I hope so," said Dr. Lovell, who searched his files and eventually found two cards. The first read:

> Avery, O. T. and Dubos, R. (1931)
> The protective action of a specific enzyme against Type III pneumococcus infection in mice.
> J. Exp. Med. 54   73-
> (N.B. for penicillin filtrate).

The second card read:

> Dubos, R. and Avery, O. T. (1931)
> Decomposition of the capsular polysaccharide of pneumococcus Type III by a bacterial enzyme.
> J. Exp. Med. 54   51-
> (N.B. for penicillin filtrate).

It revealed another extraordinary chance in the remarkable story of penicillin. As we know, Dr. Lovell was using the pneumococcus to test the potency of Raistrick's penicillin. If he had tested the penicillin against a direct pneumococcal infection of mice—and these references clearly prove that it was his intention to do so, had he remained on the staff of the London School of Hygiene—the whole history of penicillin might have been changed.

CHAPTER IV

THE THIRD ATTEMPT

Thus it came about that two determined efforts to solve the mysteries of penicillin were frustrated, and the magic drug which possessed the power to save millions of lives was relegated to the laboratory routine of killing off unwanted germs to enable purer strains of the influenza bacillus to be grown. Fleming had exercised all his talents in a vain attempt to wrest from nature the secret of penicillin. He felt sure that he was on the track of some extraordinary antiseptic that did not injure the white cells of the human body, but it was beyond his scientific skill to find the proof he needed. As for Professor Raistrick, had he realized that the treacly glaze on the glass dish contained a wonderful chemotherapeutic substance, he would probably not have ceased work until he had torn its secret out of the viscous mass. But he did not know, and turned to other researches.

Meanwhile up in smoky Sheffield another man had been working quietly to utilize the powers of penicillin to heal the sick. His story has hitherto remained untold and it was only a chance remark by Professor Florey which enabled me to relate it here. This worker was Dr. C. G. Paine who had studied medicine under Fleming at St. Mary's Medical School in Paddington. I thought that he might have been induced to carry out his experiments by seeing Fleming treat a few patients with penicillin in St. Mary's Hospital. But this was not the case. It was Fleming's account in the *British Journal of Experimental Pathology* which spurred him on and it was Fleming who supplied a culture of the mould from the laboratory of St. Mary's Hospital. Following closely Fleming's instructions in the paper, Dr. Paine prepared the penicillin filtrate and tested its activity against a strain of staphylococcus obtained from a carbuncle, by the same method that Fleming had devised. This was his test germ, and he used it throughout to check the strength of the penicillin which different batches of the mould elaborated in the broth. He had of course to create his own unit of measurement, which he did by calculating the distance from the source over which the penicillin was potent against the germs.

He was puzzled at the disparity in the strength of the penicillin in different batches of broth. One lot of broth might give him only two units, while another might give him eight. These units, dependent as they were upon quite a different system of measurement to the present Oxford system, do not give us a true idea of the potency of his extracts as compared with those of to-day; but by his system of measurement he found that the penicillin in the broth ranged from two to nine units.

Having prepared sufficient mould filtrate, he then started to try its effect on patients. The first three cases were suffering from chronic staphylococcal infections of the skin. They seemed to be ideal cases on which to test the penicillin, for they were infected by the very germs which penicillin could destroy in the laboratory, and as the dermatologist who attended them had found that they would not respond to ordinary treatment, it was considered that a trial of penicillin was justified. Accordingly they were treated with dressings soaked in the filtered broth, fresh applications being made every four hours. There was no change at the end of the first day, neither could any change be seen at the end of the second day. Three, four, five days passed, and as there was no improvement after one week, the treatment was discontinued.

Any man who carried out such a test might find some justification in considering that penicillin was quite useless; and Dr. Paine summed it up thus: "The results were uniformly disappointing, and looking back over them, in view of the low penicillin content and the presence of nutrient material in the filtrates, it is not surprising that no good results were obtained."

But while these tests were going on, penicillin was also being tried on four babies with infections of the eye who were under the care of the assistant opthalmic surgeon. In two of these the infection was caused by the staphylococcus, whereas the other two were infected by the gonococcus which causes the sex disease of gonorrhoea, the babies having contracted the disease from their mothers at birth. Here again the filtrate of penicillin was administered every four hours. In three of these cases the response was soon noticeable; within three days the two babies infected with the gonococcus were cured and so was one of the babies with the staphylococcal infection. But the other baby did not respond to this early penicillin treatment.

Here, so far as I can trace, were the very first human cases of gonococcal infection being cured by penicillin, the first hint that penicillin was to prove itself the finest cure for gonorrhoea yet discovered, something that was so deadly to the germ that it astonished the medical world by curing cases of gonorrhoea in twenty-four hours, a record beaten later by the specialists of the Royal Navy who now cure cases of this disease with six injections of penicillin in twelve hours. As for the baby with the staphylococcal infection who could not be cured, it is possible that the penicillin filtrates were too weak, as they evidently were for the skin cases. On the other hand, this resistant infection may have been the first indication of something which puzzled the later workers, who found a strain of staphylococcus which resisted the drug while other staphylococci were susceptible to it.

There was one other case in which penicillin filtrate was used in Sheffield. It was that of a colliery manager who was injured down the pit by a small piece of stone which penetrated his right eye and lodged partly behind the pupil. When he was first seen by the ophthalmic surgeon, the eyeball and eyelids were so swollen that it looked as though the sufferer might lose the sight of that eye. As is usual before all operations on the eye, swabs were taken to see if the outside of the eye was free of harmful germs, and in this case the swabs gave a pure culture of pneumococci, the germs which may cause pneumonia and which are capable of doing extensive damage if they invade the inside of the eyeball. Now the pneumococcus is vulnerable to penicillin, and so it was decided to administer the penicillin filtrate to the eye to clear up the infection before the operation was attempted. For forty-eight hours the eye was irrigated with the filtrate and gradually the grave tension in the eyeball subsided, and after a further swab had shown that the pneumococci had been banished, the operation was carried out and the chip of stone removed without further trouble or complication. It was lucky for the patient that the crude penicillin was available, for he recovered normal vision in the injured eye.

So in the year 1931, whilst Fleming was continuing his experiments with penicillin and potassium tellurite, and Raistrick was trying all he knew to isolate the substance, parallel tests were being made in Sheffield on human cases. Fleming had already treated some cases by applying dressings soaked in penicillin to infected parts, and the most he could say was that penicillin did no harm. The same could be said about the Sheffield skin cases. In effect, it did no harm, but it was equally true that it did no good, and this was as discouraging as anything could be. The facts were puzzling. Fleming's experiments indicated that the staphylococcus was highly susceptible to penicillin, yet the clinical applications seemed to oppose the laboratory findings. The balance in this topsy-turvy state of things was to some extent restored by the other four successful cases, which indeed gave grounds for hope. The swift cures of the gonococcal infection in the eyes of the two innocent babies pointed the way to a miracle. The eyes of the babies were opened and made to see clearly by the skill of the medical men. Were the doctors themselves at that important moment blind to all the portents?

I think not. On the contrary, so impressed was the Sheffield worker by these cases that during a discussion he mentioned to Professor Florey, then Professor of Pathology at Sheffield, how he had used Fleming's penicillin in the treatment of gonococcal infections of the eye, and that chance remark to Professor Florey enabled me to write this unknown chapter in the history of penicillin.

Why were these early experiments not continued? To try something new and obtain fifty per cent of cures at a first attempt would have been regarded by most people as very encouraging. Set out on a percentage basis, the record is imposing enough, but owing to the small number of cases, this way of assessing results can be very misleading, and the medical world would certainly not accept judgment on so few cases: it demands a large number of cases spread over a fair period of time before it will acknowledge and recognize any new curative agent. This makes the way of the pioneer hard, but it does sometimes protect the public. Other facts conspired to stop this attempt to ulitize penicillin in general treatment. In the first place, there was the extraordinary instability of penicillin and its variation in potency; and then again, a certain strain of one culture might produce nine units for two or three generations and later generations would yield no penicillin at all. This mutation was baffling and seemingly could not be prevented. Its cause was not known and it remains one of the peculiarities of *Penicillium notatum* still to be solved.

This difficulty was a continual source of trouble and eventually all further attempts to treat patients were given up. In Dr. Paine's own words we can find the explanation. "The variability of the strain of *Penicillium* and my transfer to a different line of work led me to neglect further investigation of the possibilities of penicillin, an omission which, as you may well imagine, I have often regretted since."

He made a fine effort to apply penicillin for the treatment of human beings, but was defeated by the strange peculiarities of the mould which sometimes yielded the drug and at other times did not.

CHAPTER V

THE FOURTH ATTEMPT

Ir seemed as if Fate had allowed that rare spore to drift through the open window down on to Fleming's plate to taunt him with a realization of its wonderful potentialities while for ever denying the world the boon of penicillin. The men who had striven so hard to unmask the mould had found the answers to a number of problems, but no one knew how many more remained to be solved. That such complexity could exist in a seemingly simple mould was incredible, yet this lowly fungus baffled some of the keenest scientific brains in Britain.

Then the United States took up the challenge and began to try to unravel the mystery of Fleming's organism and the interest shifted from London and Sheffield to the State College of Pennsylvania where Dr. Roger D. Reid of the Division of Bacteriology studied Fleming's paper in the *Journal of Pathology* and sensed the same wonders as the Scottish scientist. Could he do what Fleming had failed to do? Could he strip the mysteries from this fungus one by one until the inner magic of penicillin was laid bare? These were the questions which Dr. Reid must have pondered in his mind. He had sufficient faith in himself to believe that he could succeed, for had he considered the quest hopeless he would not have started on it. He did not doubt Dr. Fleming's scientific attainments. Quite apart from all Fleming's other work which was on record, the paper on penicillin gave proof of abilities of a very high order. Yet with true scientific instinct Dr. Reid wondered if some slight factor had been overlooked, a factor which might lead to some variation in the results. That was the point he made up his mind to settle.

As soon as Dr. Reid had reached a decision, he determined to make an effort with all the scientific resources he could command. Dr. Charles Thom, the world authority on moulds, who was a member of the United States Department of Agriculture, was available for consultation on any mycological problems that might arise, and before Dr. Reid was ready to settle down to experiment with Fleming's moulds there was an important question which he was anxious to answer. Did any other mould produce a substance similar to that which Fleming had found? Fleming asked himself the same question and experimented with several moulds which did not produce any penicillin. But Dr. Reid knew there were many more moulds which had not been tested and until they were tested it was impossible to state definitely whether they did or did not yield any substance comparable to penicillin. If a similar substance could be found in another mould, it would, of course, be a new discovery and would offer a fine field for further researches.

Accordingly Dr. Reid sought to clear the ground and find out whether penicillin was a rare substance or whether something similar was produced by other moulds. He put out a few requests for moulds to other laboratories and asked Dr. Thom to examine and name them so that their identity should be beyond doubt. Then the weeks and months were filled with making medium to suit various moulds and sowing the spores on the medium. Incubators were adjusted to attain the particular temperatures in which the moulds flourished and in due course the crops were harvested, the flasks emptied and the medium passed through a Berkefield filter to remove the mould and other solids. Then came the preparation of the plates which were sown with a test germ, as Fleming had suggested.

Dr. Reid, using a strain of *Staphylococcus aureus*, tested the filtrate from the mould *Mucer mucedo* and the germ flourished; he tested the product of *Mucer piriformis*, with the same result. *Rhizopus nigricans* yielded nothing but disappointment.

The American scientist was not dismayed. He was prepared for a long search as he settled down to work with some of the *Aspergilli*. The months passed. The records grew from *Aspergillus glaucus* to *A. nidulans*, from *A. niger* to *A. flavus*, but not one of these moulds yielded anything like penicillin. Then he began to culture and test some of the *Penicillia* among which it was reasonable to expect that he might have a little better luck and find one which yielded something resembling penicillin. Down in his records went *Penicillium expansum* and when the test was done and the record written up there was nothing to show for his work but the certain knowledge that *P. expansum* did not produce penicillin. It was the same with *P. digitatum*, *P. italicum*, *P. rubens*, *P. rubrum*, *P. roqueforti*, which ripens Roquefort cheese, *Cladosporium herbarum*, *Cephalothecium roseum*, *Hormondendrum cladosporioides*—they were such tiny moulds to carry such monumental names. He tested *P. notatum* (Westling), and *P. chrysogenum* as Raistrick had done—with similar results. His was the true scientific spirit. He cannot be too highly praised. Not until Dr. Reid had tested twenty-three different moulds would his critical mind admit that it was rare for a mould to behave like Fleming's organism and yield penicillin.

As these researches of Dr. Reid were started at the end of 1930, the potentialities of Fleming's observations must have struck him soon after Fleming's paper arrived in the United States. Securing his first culture of Fleming's organism from Dr. Thom in November, 1930, he applied for another in July, 1931. During this period and for over a year longer he continued his investigations.

By the time he had assured himself that all these other moulds yielded nothing that would inhibit the growth of germs, he was prepared to settle down to see if he could solve the final problems of penicillin. Luckily Raistrick's paper, published in October, 1932, had arrived in the United States and Dr. Reid was able to study it and use the synthetic medium on which Raistrick first grew the mould.

So Dr. Reid began to grow in glass flasks two batches of Fleming's mould, one on a veal broth and the other on the chemical medium used by Raistrick. He found, as Raistrick had stated, that the mould thrived and attained maturity much sooner on the broth than on the chemical medium and he was able to harvest the mould grown on the broth in from seven to ten days, while he cultured the mould on the synthetic medium for from twenty to twenty-five days before it was ripe for harvesting. He watched the mould begin to colour the medium with a vivid yellow pigment soon after the mycelium bloomed and started to spore, and he learned that by leaving the mould to continue its growth the vivid yellow colour gradually changed into a deep orange tone.

Reid modified Fleming's gutter method for testing the liquid filtered from the mould. He divided the glass Petri dishes across the centre. Into one half he poured his agar medium on which the germs could grow, and when the jelly was set he removed the strip across the centre of the dish and filled the empty half of the dish with a mixture composed of agar and the filtered liquid from the mould. There was nothing to prevent the penicillin in one half of the agar from diffusing out into the other half. Taking his platinum loop, he streaked his germs across both sides of the plate in continuous lines, and by trial and error began to test out various germs against the penicillin filtrate from the veal broth and the chemical broth.

Sometimes he got results which puzzled him. They were the unexpected things which happened to obstruct all those who sought to learn the inner secret of penicillin. But Dr. Reid continued his researches. If his germs grew freely on the side of the plate containing the agar and failed to grow on the side containing the mixture of agar and penicillin he knew his test had been successful. In this way he tested one germ after another and confirmed Fleming's findings.

Was there, he wondered, some characteristic that was common to all the germs that were affected by penicillin? And was there a factor common to all the germs which thrived in spite of penicillin? If there was some characteristic common to one group or the other it might provide an important clue to the mystery of penicillin. Dr. Reid planned to settle this point. He prepared glass slides of all the germs under test, stained them with Gram's stain in the way taught to bacteriologists the world over, slipped the slides on the stage of his microscope and studied them intently, looking at the way they stained, noting every little point of resemblance and difference. Then he tested his germs to see if he could learn anything new from the way in which they grew, whether they could sustain life at the same temperatures on the same foods, whether they grew faster or slower or ceased to grow at all, noting all the similarities and the differences while he carried on investigations into the physiology of the various germs.

Any hopes he may have had about this series of experiments were disappointed. Certainly he was a little wiser and had increased the sum of human knowledge, but what he learned seemed to make the mystery of penicillin more baffling than ever. In the whole group of germs affected by penicillin, there was not one factor, apart from their sensitivity, in which they were all alike; if there had been one factor common to them all, this one little point on which they were identical might have laid them all open to attack by penicillin. But there was no point on which they were identical. Nor did the germs which were immune from penicillin possess one point, except their immunity, on which they were identical, so the scientist could find no common factor which was responsible for their immunity. Indeed the puzzle was made more puzzling because both groups of germs had characteristics resembling each other.

Finishing these researches, Dr. Reid put in train some experiments to see how the penicillin affected the germs, whether it lysed them, or dissolved them, as Fleming stated in his paper, or whether it merely prevented them from multiplying. Now Fleming in his paper claimed that penicillin was bacteriolytic and bactericidal, which means that it not only killed germs, but also dissolved them. On the evidence of Fleming's plate alone I would have sworn that

OPPOSITE: *Operators at the Glaxo bottle plant at Watford inoculating the saucepan-shaped flasks with the spores of* Penicillium notatum. *Below are three agar plates cultured by Sir Alexander Fleming to show the growth of the mould at five, seven and ten days.*

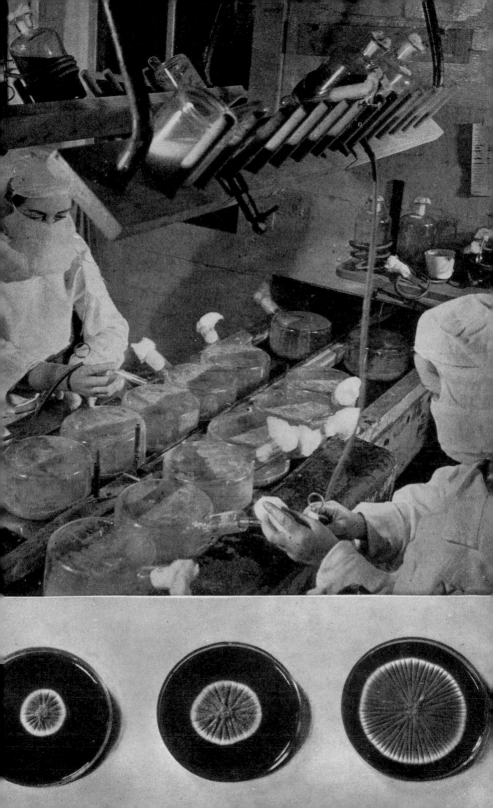

penicillin was lytic, too. But Dr. Reid as the result of his experiments said that the germs were not destroyed, but merely inhibited, or prevented from growing. If this were true, it indicated that penicillin was not bacteriolytic, nor bactericidal, but that it was bacteriostatic. This meant that it could not kill the germs, but that it merely prevented them from multiplying and that the germs were then overcome by some other agents in some other way. Fleming believed one thing and Dr. Reid believed another. Both had obtained experimental proofs of their beliefs. Who was right? This difference of opinion concerning the way penicillin acted developed later on into something of a controversy as is disclosed in a subsequent chapter.

With that point cleared up, as he thought, Dr. Reid sought the answer to another question—was the penicillin destroyed by light. Obtaining some flasks made of a special glass that would allow the ultra-violet rays to pass, he grew the mould in these flasks. Every day for fifteen minutes an arc lamp was switched on over the flasks. It was fitted with a quartz filter that allowed the infra-red rays and ultra-violet rays to pass. Naturally Dr. Reid shielded the growing cultures from the heat of the lamp to avoid harming them and he took every scientific precaution to prevent his cultures becoming contaminated with other germs.

Not one drop of penicillin did he obtain. The medium looked the same, it attained the same yellow colour, but it had no power to stop the test germs growing. Whether the mould could not produce any penicillin under the light, or whether the light destroyed the penicillin as it was produced, the American scientist did not know. All he knew was that the medium was inactive.

Having set his mind at rest on this point, he began work on another series of experiments which he had every reason to believe would be fruitful. Oxygen is necessary to most forms of life and lack of it will lead to death. Many an acute case of pneumonia has been saved by fitting a mask over the face and allowing the patient to breathe pure oxygen for considerable periods every day. Exceptions exist. There are some germs which cannot live in the ordinary atmosphere. The scientist names them anaerobes or anaerobic, and to these germs oxygen means death. Dr. Reid was well aware of the important part oxygen played in helping most germs to produce their poisons or toxins. From this fact he argued that additional oxygen might produce a greater yield of penicillin than ever, and he pondered over the best way to prove the fact.

E—m

In the end he arranged to pass oxygen through the medium below the growing mould at the rate of a hundred bubbles of oxygen a minute for a quarter of an hour each day until the mould was ready for harvesting, and above the mould itself he maintained a supply of oxygen gas all the time. But when Dr. Reid came to test the filtered medium he could trace no penicillin at all. He was not only baffled, but extremely disappointed. The result was contrary to all his anticipations. He grew the mould with additional hydrogen gas and carbon dioxide in the same way, with the same results—no penicillin was to be found.

Despite his disappointment, the American scientist pursued his task with unabated vigour and turned now to solve the problem of isolating the penicillin. Having studied what Raistrick had done, Dr. Reid wondered if he could isolate penicillin by distilling the filtrate at a low temperature and a low pressure. Having finished the distillation, he took a sample of what he hoped would be a very concentrated form of penicillin and tested it. To his great surprise the penicillin had completely disappeared. Wondering if it had been left behind in the residue, he tested the residue that was left over from the distillation. Again he could find no trace of penicillin. The penicillin which was certainly present when he started the experiment had simply vanished. This left him more than ever puzzled by the peculiar behaviour of the mysterious substance produced by Fleming's mould.

Unable to isolate the penicillin by distillation, he next attempted to separate it from the medium by allowing it to diffuse out into distilled water—the scientist uses the term dialyse—in the hope that he might recover it from the water if the experiment succeeded. So he poured his bright yellow filtered medium into collodian bags which he placed in distilled water. The way that the distilled water began to turn yellow soon indicated that some diffusion was taking place through the collodian skin of the bags and after leaving the bags in the water for thirty-six hours he removed them to test the contents. Again the penicillin had disappeared. It was not in the distilled water. It was not left behind in the collodian bags. How it had escaped and where it had gone remained mysteries.

Although Raistrick was convinced by his experiments that the chrysogenin, as he called the yellow pigment, and the penicillin were two separate substances, Dr. Reid maintained an open mind on the question and wondered whether the yellow pigment and penicillin were indeed one and the same thing. By filtering some of the yellow fluid through charcoal he was able to remove the yellow pigment. When he tested the remaining fluid he found that there was no penicillin in it at all. For the moment it looked as though there was something in the idea that the pigment and the penicillin were the same thing. But after juggling with some chloroform to remove the yellow pigment, he found that the penicillin in the filtered medium was as strong as ever. This seemed to nullify the result of the previous experiment. After further work, he was forced to conclude that the yellow colouring matter and the penicillin were in fact two separate and distinct substances.

Still unbeaten, he tried to extract the penicillin with acetone. He failed. Then he tried to extract the elusive substance with ether as Fleming had tried and failed again. Raistrick, however, had succeeded in extracting the penicillin with ether, so here was a point on which the British scientist was in advance of the American.

Then Dr. Reid wondered whether the action of penicillin on the germs had anything to do with the surface tension of the medium, so he began a series of measurements with a delicate instrument known as a tensiometer to test the tension on the surface of some veal medium containing penicillin; secondly, some chemical medium containing penicillin and, thirdly, the medium before any mould was planted on it. The results convinced him that the action of penicillin on the germs was nothing to do with surface tension.

His repeated efforts to wrest the penicillin out of the filtered medium led him to discover several enzymes, namely erypsin, catalase, lipase, amylase, trypsin and amidase, but the penicillin which he had sought for years eluded him.

So Fleming's humble mould defeated this long-sustained American effort to wrest from it the secret of penicillin.

CHAPTER VI

A VITAL DECISION

IN the laboratories of St. Mary's Hospital and the Lister Institute and other British laboratories Fleming's mould continued to grow unobtrusively in its test tubes. The men who sensed that something wonderful might be hidden away in it had sought in vain for the secret which Nature had concealed too cleverly for them to discover. Thus the mould flourished in the hospital laboratories while the patients whom it might have saved continued to die in the hospital wards until Dr. Howard Florey devoted his powers to solving the mystery.

Florey was an Australian with all the friendliness and forcefulness of the nation that is developing and opening up the great island continent. Born in the South Australian capital of Adelaide on September 24, 1898, Howard Walter Florey began to take an interest in science when he was a boy and there was nothing he liked better than to get hold of a book on popular science which he could browse upon for days. The life and work of a scientist thus made an early appeal to him, and his lessons at St. Peter's Collegiate School developed an interest in chemistry which he never lost.

"I liked chemistry at school," he remarked, "and I was allowed to do what I wanted." He was fortunate in having parents who permitted him to follow his bent.

From school he went to Adelaide University where he took his medical degree of M.B. and incidentally displayed more than a passing interest in another medical student, Miss Ethel Reed, who obtained her medical degree about the same time and married him some years later. In their graduate days they had decided opinions as to what they wanted to do. She was keen on the clinical side of medicine, while he was determined never to be a general practitioner, but to devote his life to research. There was thus no possible conflict in their careers which, in the end, proved to be complementary to each other.

Winning a Rhodes Scholarship which took him to Magdalen College, Oxford, Florey settled down to study physiology. He had barely taken his B.A. degree in physiology when one of the professors suggested that it would be a good thing for him to go in for pathology. The idea appealed to Florey who went to Cambridge in 1924 to work in pathology under Professor Dean.

Academic honours piled up in the next few years as degree followed degree. When he landed in England in 1922 he was a Bachelor of Medicine of Adelaide University. In due course he became a Master of Arts, a Bachelor of Science and a Doctor of Philosophy to prove how wide was his knowledge. Yet he was no pedant. His learning sat lightly on his shoulders. He was sure of himself, very alert in body and brain, with a strong nose and jaw to convey a hint of the forcefulness of his character. In conversation, his swift mental reactions were reflected by a flashing eye and jerk of the head to show how quickly he had caught an idea before it was half uttered.

"He was always a jump ahead of us," said one of the scientists who helped to work out penicillin at Oxford. "If we were halted by a problem, he would suggest a way out. If one of us was hesitating between several possible ways of doing a thing, he would urge us to get on with it in the way which we had already proved possible."

He was therefore a good leader as well as a fine scientist, which goes to explain why he and the team of scientists whom he led were able to give penicillin to the world after four previous attempts by other scientists had failed.

It happened that in 1925 Dr. Florey visited the United States as a Rockefeller Foundation Fellow to work for a while in some of the laboratories to gain further knowledge and experience. For several months he settled down in the University of Pennsylvania in Philadelphia where he worked in the laboratory of Dr. A. N. Richards, and when they parted each was left with the memory of a pleasant association. Enlarging his experience in other American laboratories, Florey at length returned to London where he worked for a time as a Freedom Research Fellow at the London Hospital before going on to Cambridge where in 1929 he became interested in Fleming's discovery of lysozyme. The magical properties of dissolving harmless germs which was possessed by this constituent of saliva and tears and white of egg made a strong appeal to the scientist. Fleming and other workers knew what lysozyme could do, but its chemical composition was unknown.

To Florey, the distribution and action of lysozyme presented an attractive field for research, and quite by chance he began to work on the subject in the same year that Fleming published his paper on penicillin. Starting his researches on lysozyme alone in Cambridge, he then collaborated with Goldsworthy, and continued to maintain his interest in the subject when he became Professor of Pathology at Sheffield University. It was during the early part of his stay in Sheffield that Dr. Paine touched on the experiments with penicillin, an incident that was recalled by Florey some twelve years later when he mentioned it to me. Florey's interest, however, was concentrated on lysozyme and he gave no thought to penicillin except to register in his mind that Dr. Paine had cured a gonococcal infection of the eye and had found the mould too variable to cope with.

I thought it possible that the cures which Dr. Paine had effected with penicillin might have influenced Florey to deal with penicillin some years afterwards; but he assured me that the incident did not influence him at all, and that if it had done so it would probably have influenced him against investigating penicillin owing to the fact that Dr. Paine, who was a clever bacteriologist, could not control the mould which did not always produce penicillin.

In 1935 Florey left Sheffield University to become Professor of Pathology in the Sir William Dunn School of Pathology at Oxford University. Here amid the most beautiful sylvan surroundings he kept his work going on lysozyme and Dr. Roberts, whom he charged with the task, succeeded in 1937 in obtaining it in a pure state. In the same year Dr. E. P. Abraham who was working nearby in the Dyson Perrins Laboratory succeeded in crystallizing it. Lysozyme, it may be mentioned, is a ferment, or enzyme. These substances possess the remarkable property of being able to produce fermentation in the absence of living cells. In the case of lysozyme, it dissolves the harmless germs by fermentation in a few seconds, and the power as well as the rapidity are alike impressive.

Some time after Florey went to the School of Pathology at Oxford, he invited Dr. E. B. Chain to develop the chemical section, an invitation that was gladly accepted. Chain, who had taken a German degree in chemistry, had continued his work at Cambridge where he took the degree of Ph.D. in 1935. Now he settled down to work in Oxford.

About five feet six inches in height, with long black hair, dark eyes and a sharp, well-cut nose, Dr. Chain was full of nervous energy, very temperamental and not the sort of man to suffer fools gladly. He spoke incisively on his own subject and when launched on a discussion was apt to pace up and down his laboratory with nervous steps, his dark eyes flashing, his hands waving and shoulders shrugging to play their part in making his points.

When I first saw him hunched up in his chair bending over a technical work on his bench, his long black hair hanging down each side of his face like a curtain, I was struck by his resemblance to Einstein, except that the colour of his hair was different. At other times when his hair was brushed straight back, he bore a resemblance to Stalin. A clever pianist, he might have made a mark as a musician if his love of science had been less strong.

He was fertile in ideas, the very type to cut away from routine and think out new ways of doing new things. His work which disclosed the chemical action of lysozyme stimulated him to take an interest in similar lytic agents, so called because they dissolve or lyse germs. "People may think that this work on lysozyme led me to investigate Fleming's other discovery of penicillin, but that was not the case at all," he said. "I was searching for lytic agents with powers similar to that of lysozyme. It was pure scientific research, solely of academic importance. Accordingly I began to make a big search of the literature, reading day after day and week after week to see what I could find dealing with the subject."

This was a laborious task, needing much patience. But fortunately the University of Oxford in the Radcliffe Science Library possessed a fine library containing a wide range of scientific journals published in many countries of the world, so these were available for examination on the spot.

"I did not find many lytic substances," continued Dr. Chain. "But I did find a number of papers dealing with germs which produced substances that affected other germs and stopped them from growing. Being a biochemist, I said to myself, 'here is a field of interest to a chemist.' There are many known substances which have an antibacterial action, although their chemistry is entirely unknown. Among them was an interesting substance known as pyocyanase which was produced by the *Bacillus pyocyaneus*.

"It was sheer luck that I came on Fleming's paper in the *British Journal of Experimental Pathology* describing penicillin. I am a biochemist, not a pathologist, and no chemist would normally think of reading a work on pathology to assist his researches in chemistry. But here in Oxford at the School of Pathology the two subjects are combined under one roof, so they are closely linked, and this direct association led me to go through the journal. I had never heard of Fleming's paper before, and I was particularly interested because penicillin affected the Gram-positive germs. But there was nothing in Fleming's paper to suggest that there was a gold mine in front of us.

"In my further search of the literature I came on Raistrick's paper describing how he had worked on penicillin and managed to grow the mould on a chemical medium from which he had recovered penicillin. Raistrick was a brilliant chemist who had specialized on moulds all his life. Nevertheless I made up my mind to see what I could find out about penicillin. I thought then that it would turn out to be an enzyme. Fleming's observation in the first place was amazingly lucky. It was no less lucky that I should have gone to the *Journal of Pathology* to read his paper, and by another lucky turn of chance I discovered that we had here on the spot, growing in the school, some cultures of the very mould, *Penicillium notatum*, which Fleming had grown at St. Mary's Hospital. I went into the laboratory of Miss Campbell-Renton, who worked here with the late Professor Dreyer, to ask her if she knew of the mould."

"We have it here. It has been growing here for years. We used it in Professor Dreyer's time—I think it was for working with virus," she said.

"I would like to work on it. How about giving me a culture?" asked Chain, who was duly presented with a culture.

"When it was received from St. Mary's Hospital and who obtained it we have not been able to trace," Chain remarked to me. "It was rather remarkable that it should be growing here in the laboratory just when I wanted it. So I obtained my culture of the mould and started to work on the problem where Professor Raistrick had left off."

Thus the work on lysozyme which had interested Professor Florey for so many years began to focus attention on penicillin. By sheer chance that rare spore alighted on Fleming's plate and raised hopes that were frustrated; by sheer chance Dr. Chain read Fleming's paper and learned about penicillin; by sheer chance this very mould which must have come from St. Mary's Hospital many years earlier was growing in the laboratory of the School of Pathology at Oxford. It was indeed remarkable.

Pondering over the subject of bacterial antagonisms which had interested him for so many years, reviewing the long line of researches which had revealed the mystery of lysozyme, Professor Florey concluded that the anti-bacterial substances offered almost a virgin field for pure research, so he discussed the matter in all its aspects with Dr. Chain. The idea appealed to both men. On the one hand Professor Florey could deal with the biological problems, while Dr. Chain could work out the chemical problems, so the work would be well divided. But much had to be done before it could be started, and Dr. Chain resumed his search of the literature until his notes were complete.

At length Dr. Chain and Professor Florey sat down together to survey the field and make a plan for the work they wanted to do. The researches they planned were purely academic, of interest to science alone. They did not plan to make a world discovery that would save countless lives. Such an idea did not enter their heads for a moment. Their aim was to explore the field of bacterial antagonisms, find out as much as they could about the way in which these unknown substances acted and discover their chemical composition. Their original intention was to conduct researches into every one of these substances that was known, but eventually they narrowed the field to three subjects, the *Bacillus pyocyaneus*, *Penicillium notatum* and *Subtilis-mesentericus*. The funds to finance these researches were eventually provided by the Medical Research Council, the Rockefeller Foundation, and the Nuffield Provincial Hospitals Trust.

For a time the two scientists hesitated in their first choice. The fact that penicillin obviously possessed peculiar chemical properties made a special appeal to Chain, that the mould was known to produce an anti-bacterial substance influenced both men, and Florey found an added interest in the fact that penicillin was potent against the staphylococcus which caused so much human suffering. They were walking home one evening discussing the problem of what to start on first when, just as they were passing under a great elm at the entrance to the park, they decided to start on penicillin.

So the die was cast.

CHAPTER VII

A PINCH OF BROWN POWDER

IT was in 1938 that they formulated their plan, but not until July, 1939, just before Germany shattered the peace of the world, were they able to begin their first experimental work on penicillin. There was little to encourage them. Fleming had been frustrated; Raistrick had been frustrated; Paine had been frustrated; Reid in the United States had made his effort and failed. Anything less hopeful would be hard to find. The astonishing thing is that neither Florey nor Chain were dissuaded by these previous failures.

"I don't think penicillin is as labile as Fleming and Raistrick make out, because it will keep in an ice chest for months, and any chemical that will do that is subject to chemical manipulation", said Chain to Professor Florey. Thus in Raistrick's work Dr. Chain found the inspiration to go on. And it was Raistrick whom they had to thank for proving that the mould could be grown on a synthetic medium, thus simplifying their work and saving time.

So the scene was set for solving the last mysteries of penicillin. The Sir William Dunn School of Pathology is a modern, red brick building of three storeys with well designed laboratories as up-to-date as anything of their kind when they were built twenty years ago. Situated in ideal surroundings on the edge of a park, it is approached down a road fringed on one side with a row of upstanding lime trees which in blossom-time cast their sweet perfume over the whole neighbourhood while the bees swarm among the flowers and add their musical drone to the wind in the leaves. Here in a restful study panelled in light oak, with book-lined shelves, a big desk and some easy chairs, Professor Florey planned the work with Dr. Chain. Through the window was a view of verdant parkland with huge elm trees mounting to the skies. All the scientific knowledge necessary to their project was here under one roof, for there was a sub-department of chemical pathology, a department of bio-chemistry, and a sub-department of bacteriology, of which Professor A. D. Gardner was the head.

Here also was Dr. Norman G. Heatley, Ph.D., whose scientific attainments included an outstanding ability in the field of micro-chemical measurements. In measuring the infinitesimal he was without peer, one of the few men in England capable of this exact and difficult work, and it was as a specialist in micro-chemical measurement that he was invited to join the School of Pathology in Oxford in 1936.

The world will never know how much it owes to Heatley for his work on penicillin. Born at Woodbridge on January 10, 1911, Heatley went to Tonbridge school before graduating at Cambridge, where he took the Natural Science Tripos and eventually after years of research he attained his Ph.D. degree. About five feet nine inches in height, he is of slender build, with a thin brown face, small mouth, dark eyes and black hair. Very modest and unassuming, he possesses a quiet manner and voice which conceal a fine scientific brain and inventive powers.

At the declaration of war on September 3, 1939, Dr. Chain was growing about a dozen flasks of Fleming's mould so that Professor Florey could test the filtered medium to see whether the Oxford strain of the mould was capable of producing penicillin. In due course it was confirmed that the filtered medium was potent and all the work carried out thenceforward at Oxford until penicillin became an accomplished fact was done with the strain of Fleming's mould that had been growing in the laboratory of the School of Pathology for years.

It happened that in August, 1939, Dr. Heatley was preparing to leave Oxford to work for a year with a Rockefeller Fellowship in the University of Copenhagen. "My bags were lying already packed when war broke out. I planned to go on the 12th or 13th of September, but my plans were knocked on the head," he said.

Thus Fate intervened at the eleventh hour to prevent Heatley from going to Copenhagen and Florey asked him to return to the School of Pathology to work on penicillin. From the beginning of October, Heatley concentrated all his abilities on producing penicillin. He assumed responsibility for the growing of the mould and settled down to tackle all the problems connected with this task. Heatley was a clever inventor, a sound scientist, so intensely interested in his work that it occupied all his thoughts. He was the type of man who, if left alone, would drive himself far harder than anyone could ever drive him.

Florey was a fine leader and a good judge of men. He did not worry Heatley, but allowed him to wrestle quietly with the scientific problems surrounding his side of the work, the problems which up to then had defeated all efforts of the scientists who had striven to solve the mystery of penicillin. Occasionally the professor would drop in to find Heatley mixing a medium or working on a piece of scientific apparatus. The two men would discuss progress, Florey would drop a suggestion and depart, while Heatley at the earliest moment would make a test to see whether there was anything in the suggestion.

He worked at first with Raistrick's synthetic medium made to the modified Czapek-Dox formula. The great drawback to this was that the mould took so long to come to maturity. Heatley sought to cut down the time to enable the mould to be harvested sooner. He had no idea that penicillin was a wonderful drug. Neither had Florey, nor Chain. But Heatley had the right idea—that the mould took too long to grow, and that every day he could save on growing it would bring the product of the mould nearer to economic production—if it proved to be worth while.

He began to pander to the taste of the mould as though he were the chef of the Savoy Hotel tickling the palate of a millionaire. He added a little pinch of this chemical to see if the mould liked it, he added a few grains of that. Every speck of the stuff that went into the chemical broth was carefully measured and checked and written up in his records in his neat upright handwriting; every detail about the growth of the mould went down. He was most precise. The black entries in his notebook were sprinkled with notes in red. The colours had their meanings. They caught the attention at once. One medium after another was tried. The behaviour of the mould was carefully noted, the mould itself was measured and its weight estimated and, most important of all, the potency of the penicillin it produced was assessed.

As the weeks slid by, Heatley experimented with fifteen variations of the original chemical medium. By adding a yeast extract he speeded up the growth of the mould from over twenty days to ten or twelve, but it did not increase the yield of penicillin, although it increased the cost. The first few batches of mould grown at Oxford yielded very little penicillin indeed, not more than two or three units per cubic centimetre, and all attempts to increase this yield met with little success.

To Florey and Chain and Heatley a unit of measurement was an absolute necessity. They would have been lost without it, like a ship without a compass. They could not have told where they were or what they were doing, whether they were going forward or sliding backward. It was as essential for them to assay the strength of the penicillin in the medium as it was for a metallurgist to assay the gold in the borings taken from a reef in order to determine its richness. Devoting his attention to the task, Heatley found a way of testing the filtered medium very simply and quickly. It was a variation of Fleming's method of cutting discs out of the agar plate with a cork borer; but Heatley used little porcelain tubes which he placed on the layer of agar in the Petri dish. He made his first tests with glass tubes, then he used some specially-made porcelain tubes with bevelled edges that were designed to sink into the agar, and at last found it was possible to make a water-tight joint simply by heating the ends of the tubes. To attain a method of measurement, a partially purified solution of penicillin was chosen as the standard and as much penicillin as was contained in one cubic centimetre of it was fixed as one unit. This standard solution, which was stored in the refrigerator, was effective against the test germs in a zone that measured about twenty-four millimetres in diameter, and by taking a cubic centimetre of the standard solution and a cubic centimetre of any new solution of unknown strength, it was possible to compare one with the other.

The test was simple. A certain quantity of the standard solution was placed in a porcelain cylinder on the agar plate, a similar quantity of the new penicillin solution was placed in another cylinder, from which it could diffuse out of the bottom into the surrounding agar. The plate was then seeded liberally with the test germ, *Staphylococcus aureus* and lodged in the incubator for from twelve to sixteen hours, when it was withdrawn for examination. If the new penicillin had escaped contamination and was potent, there would be found round the cylinder a zone where the test germ had been stopped from growing, and by comparing the width of this zone with the width of the other zone made by the standard solution, the strength of the new penicillin could be measured. This assay devised by Heatley gradually came into general use and the unit of measurement became known as the Oxford unit.

To avoid little drops of moisture condensing on the glass cover of the Petri dish and falling upon the agar, thus interfering with the test, Heatley placed his Petri dishes on strips of wood laid on the shelves of the incubator instead of directly upon the shelves. It is customary for bacteriologists to place the Petri dishes in the incubator with the cover side down in order to avoid any drops of condensation from dripping on the culture, but Heatley had to adopt a new method because the penicillin would have run out of the tubes if they had been turned upside down.

An interesting point arose when the Oxford workers sought to use this same method for measuring the amount of penicillin in human blood after injections. It was reasonable to expect that when the natural defences of the human blood were added to penicillin, the effect would be all the greater, instead of which the penicillin appeared to be less effective. At first sight this was contrary to the facts; but the reason was not far to seek. The red blood cells sank like fish scales to the bottom of the porcelain tubes and formed a fairly tight seal on top of the agar through which the penicillin could not penetrate to stop the test germs from growing. This difficulty was soon overcome by removing the red cells from the blood and using the yellow serum, or blood plasma, to carry out the test.

Meanwhile Dr. Chain came to grips with the chemical problems. He knew many methods of isolating chemical substances from liquids. He tried them all and found out that there was one thing he did not know—how to isolate penicillin. From the beginning he was handicapped by the small quantities of penicillin with which he had to work. The paucity of material throughout was indeed one of the greatest drawbacks with which the Oxford scientists had to contend and the total amount of penicillin used by them to bring their researches to success was very small. At times when they had a milligramme, or one twenty-eighth thousandth part of an ounce to work with, they counted themselves lucky.

With the available penicillin Chain confirmed that Raistrick was right in naming penicillin as an acid and later he proved that the chemical was of low molecular weight. Its molecules were so tiny that it could ooze through the pores of a cellophane membrane into the medium as easily as perspiration oozes through the sweat glands of the human skin.

But one of the early problems was to discover a way in which penicillin could be stabilized so that the Oxford workers could be certain of finding the substance to work with when they wanted it. Unfortunately they were never quite sure whether the penicillin they had started to work with still remained in the filtered liquid or whether it had disappeared. It was as though a man writing a letter suddenly found that the paper on which he was writing had dissolved into nothing under his pen. This was one of the first difficulties that Chain set himself to overcome. The clue lay in Raistrick's work. Fleming had proved that the greater the heat that was applied to penicillin, the easier it was destroyed; and Raistrick dropping down the scale of temperatures found that penicillin could be kept in an ice box for three months. Here was the key, and in the beginning of 1940 Chain had proved by a series of experiments that so long as penicillin was kept cool, it would not fly away.

It was one day about this time that Professor Florey was conferring with Dr. Chain and Dr. Heatley upon the problem of extracting the penicillin from the medium when Heatley remarked: "Why not try Raistrick's method of extracting it from the medium with ether and then shaking it with buffer to extract it from the ether."

Chain was dubious. "You may as well try it to convince yourself that it won't work," he replied.

Heatley tried it—and it worked. Thus the work done by Raistrick and his colleagues nine years earlier helped to forge another link in the chain that was to lead to ultimate success.

There was one serious difficulty. The solution had to be made acid to enable the penicillin to pass from it into the ether, yet it was known that acid rapidly destroyed the penicillin. Experiments, however, disclosed that it was possible to reduce the destructive effect of the acid by cooling the solutions, and directly the penicillin had passed into the ether it was no longer unstable—a most welcome discovery. Consequently the crude watery penicillin solution was cooled in the refrigerator, then made strongly acid and shaken with some cooled ether. After standing for some time, the ether and water separated into two layers, with nearly all the penicillin in the ether, so the water was thrown away. Then the clear ether solution was shaken up with slightly alkaline water into which the penicillin passed.

Normal evaporation of this final solution left a sticky, treacly mass which was most difficult to deal with, so it had to be dried in a frozen state. And when this was accomplished, the Oxford workers were left with a tiny pinch of brown powder.

It was the first salt of penicillin—so powerful that they imagined that they had obtained a pinch of pure penicillin. When it was diluted, one drop in 500,000 sufficed to prevent the growth of the staphylococci. Here was something with a potency undreamed of and it spurred them on to greater efforts. Yet the wonderful thing was that instead of being pure, this first salt of penicillin consisted of ninety-nine per cent of impurities. Much later when the Oxford workers obtained a highly purified form of penicillin they learned that one part of it in fifty millions would prevent staphylococci from growing, while it needed only one part of penicillin in a hundred million parts of medium to prevent gonococci from growing. They were scientists, cool, calculating, dealing only with facts, but even to them it was hardly believable—it was a miracle.

"I gave some of the material for toxicity tests and there was no toxicity," explained Dr. Chain. "That was one of the remarkable things about penicillin. Although the penicillin in the stuff we obtained was only a small percentage, and perhaps nine-tenths of it was colouring matter and other stuff, all this foreign matter was comparatively harmless. But for aught we knew the penicillin itself might have been toxic and it was within the bounds of possibility that as we reduced the foreign matter and produced penicillin in a purer form we might have produced something which grew more toxic with every stage of refinement. While one part of penicillin in ninety-nine parts of broth might be quite harmless because it was weakened by dilution, when we obtained that one drop alone it might have been a deadly poison. We did not know. But by the most amazing good fortune this extraneous stuff that was mixed with penicillin proved in the main to be innocuous."

That fact allowed penicillin to be produced in time to save thousands of men wounded in the war, for it enabled the clinical experiments to be carried out with the crude penicillin because it was harmless, despite its impurities, instead of waiting until the penicillin had been purified and crystallized.

OPPOSITE: *Dr. E. B. Chain, who collaborated with Dr. Abraham in isolating, purifying and drying penicillin. The white column on the left, with the flask beneath, is the column of powdered alumina which enabled them to achieve success, as described in the text.*

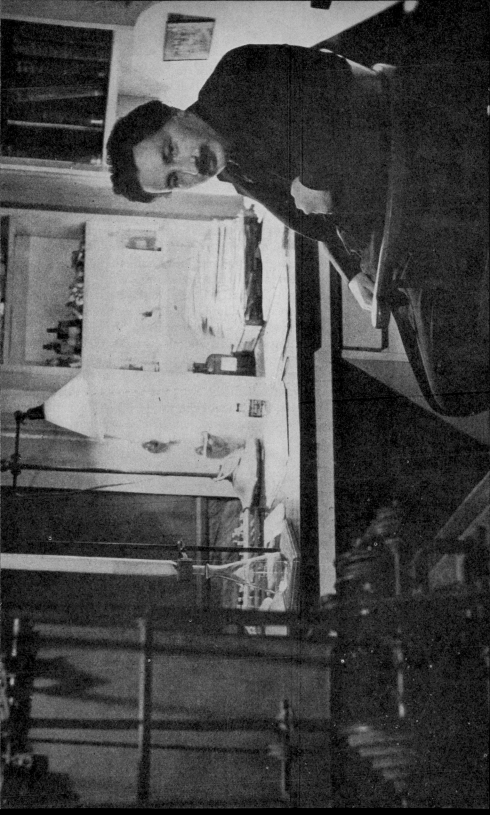

CHAPTER VIII

THE MIRACLE

ALL was quiet, uncannily quiet on the Western Front during these early months of 1940. But in the laboratories of the Sir William Dunn School of Pathology at Oxford, work went on at high pressure. "It went on simultaneously in all departments, upstairs and downstairs," said Professor Florey.

They were keyed up and determined to wrest the secret of penicillin from the humble mould which produced it. The mould itself resembled the unknown quantity dubbed in mathematics as x. No one could tell definitely what it would do. Sometimes it produced penicillin and sometimes it did not. In both cases the mould flourished as usual and the medium became yellow, but often the precious penicillin which ought to have been there was missing. Of course the first thought was that the mould had become contaminated with other bacteria which had destroyed the penicillin. But in some cases this was not true. Heatley could not find the slightest sign of contamination. What he ultimately discovered was that growing among the colonies of mould capable of producing penicillin were colonies of the mould which did not produce any penicillin. In appearance the two moulds were exactly similar. No one could tell the difference between the active and inactive except by testing them for penicillin. If spores from inactive colonies were used to plant a batch of medium, there was no penicillin. And if these inactive colonies were allowed to grow with the active colonies they might perhaps destroy the penicillin produced by the active mould. Imagine how this complicated the work. These mutations of the mould which produced no penicillin generally came into existence when the mould was past the first flush of growth and had reached old age. The unusual thing about these strains was that although in the mass they produced no penicillin, it was possible by selecting spores from them to grow colonies of mould which produced a good yield, colonies which produced a small yield and colonies which produced no penicillin at all. Heatley did his best to counter this tendency by reserving some master strains of the mould from which to grow his cultures, and a similar course was adopted later by commercial concerns.

OPPOSITE: Dr. E. P. Abraham, the young Oxford chemist, who collaborated with Dr. E. B. Chain in isolating, purifying and drying penicillin in powder form. The amazing story of how he first found the crystals of pure penicillin after repeated failures is told on page 154.

By May, 1940, when the German tanks were destroying France and forcing the British Army back to Dunkirk, Heatley and Chain had managed with great difficulty to extract and collect enough crude penicillin to enable Professor Florey to make an initial test on mice. In the test tube the penicillin had emerged successfully from all experiments; it had done as much, if not more, than Florey expected, but whether it would act in the living organism as it had acted in the test tube was still an open question. Eleven years earlier, Fleming had injected the filtered broth of penicillin into mice and rabbits and found that it had no more toxic effects than ordinary broth. But what Professor Florey was anxious to learn was whether penicillin would save mice from dying when they were injected with lethal doses of germs. It was the crucial test. Upon it depended the whole future of penicillin.

Accordingly on May 25, 1940, Professor Florey ordered his technical assistant Mr. Kent to bring up eight mice. They were the white mice used in all laboratory tests, housed in round cages of glass, twelve inches in diameter, which could easily be sterilized, with covers of perforated zinc. A little chaff was scattered on the bottom of the cages with a few oats and a scrap of biscuit for the mice to nibble at.

With dexterity that came from experience, Kent picked each mouse up by the tail and swung it to his coat sleeve, with another easy movement he caught it by the back of the neck and turned it over for injection, before dropping it back in its cage. An hour later, when the germs were circulating in the blood stream, Professor Florey injected four of the mice with penicillin, and used the other four as controls. All were injected with the same dose of germs, and if the controls died and the others lived it would prove that the penicillin was effective. The dose of penicillin which Florey gave the mice was quite small, one-hundredth of a cubic centimetre and he gave one pair of mice a single dose of penicillin, while he injected the others at intervals with five doses in all.

This first test was made on a Saturday and as Florey left the laboratory that evening the control mice were not looking very happy. Heatley, immersed in the experiment, was so anxious to learn whether the work had been successful that he remained at the laboratory to see what happened to the mice. Darkness fell and he still busied himself in his laboratory, taking an occasional look at the mice. The coats of the controls began to fluff out. They were obviously sick. The two mice which had been injected with one dose of penicillin did not look quite so sleek as the other pair which had been given five injections. Midnight struck on the Oxford clocks and still Heatley remained to watch the white mice. First one, then another of the untreated mice died until by 3.45 on the morning of Sunday, May 26, the four controls were dead, while the other four mice which had been treated with penicillin were still alive, although the two which received one dose were not looking too well.

That young English scientist alone in the laboratory in Oxford felt a strange elation. All the difficulties they had jointly overcome, all the difficulties that faced them were forgotten. Penicillin was a success. He had no doubts about it. Wrapped in thought, he barely remembered taking out his cycle, getting into the saddle and pedalling through the darkness for home.

"Halt!" shouted a voice.

Heatley, with a jolt, realized that he was cycling and moved to put on the brakes. They did not act very well.

"Halt! Who goes there!" shouted the voice menacingly.

Heatley came to a stop with squeaking brakes and got off, to find a Home Guard almost on top of him.

"What are you doing at this time of night?" asked the Home Guard, flashing his torch on the scientist.

Heatley explained and was permitted to ride on. But he does not remember turning the pedals—they seemed to turn themselves and he floated along on air. In all the world, he was the first man to see penicillin perform its miracle in the silence of that Oxford laboratory during the stilly night, and he had helped to bring the miracle about. No wonder he was excited.

And that voice in the darkness which halted him in his tracks proved that England was on guard.

Later that Sunday morning Professor Florey and Dr. Chain went to the laboratory to see the result of the experiment. Chain smiled and shrugged, his cheeks flushed with excitement and his eyes sparkled as he gazed at the dead controls and watched the treated mice still alive in their cages.

"It looks very promising," the Professor remarked and began to plan another mouse experiment for the next day. Despite his outward calm, he was excited at the possibilities that were opened up. Here was the first proof that penicillin was no antiseptic, as Fleming thought, but a true chemotherapeutic substance, one of the things the medical scientist continually dreams about and seldom discovers. Although the mice treated with one dose of penicillin both died afterwards, the fact did not worry him. It merely proved that he had not given them enough penicillin. The survival of the other two mice proved that penicillin in sufficient quantities was effective. The key to all their problems was more penicillin.

Heatley, feeling very tired after his long vigil, arrived at the laboratory to find the Professor and Dr. Chain looking very pleased with the results of the experiment. Such a marked success clearly indicated that penicillin might prove to be of great value in the treatment of war wounds, and the urgency of the matter decided them to call on their colleagues in the school to make a co-operative effort. Accordingly Professor A. D. Gardner, professor of bacteriology, Dr. M. A. Jennings, a pathologist, and Dr. E. P. Abraham, an organic chemist, were invited to collaborate in the work and they gladly consented, thus the famous "Oxford team" was formed.

"We must increase production," said Professor Florey to Heatley during that memorable conference. "I want you to produce a hundred litres a week."

It meant a big expansion. And to deal with these quantities it was essential to devise some method of automatic extraction. Yet Heatley, who had a better idea of the difficulties than any living man, was not deterred. At once his mind began to ponder on the problems. But he was so tired and the thoughts kept racing through his mind so fast that he did not sleep a wink that Sunday night.

Next morning, May 27, 1940, Dr. Jennings entered the laboratory to find ten mice in their glass cages which Kent had arranged on the benches. One by one Kent swung them up on his sleeve and turned them over for Dr. Jennings to inject with streptococci. An hour later Professor Florey injected six of them with penicillin and used the other four as controls. By the third day three of the controls were dead and the six treated mice were well and lively.

One thing was obvious to Professor Florey, the necessity of giving the mice a more virulent dose of germs that would kill them with certainty within twenty-four hours. So on May 28 sixteen mice were injected with double the previous dose of germs. Setting aside six to act as controls, Professor Florey injected the others with graduated doses of penicillin to try to find out the minimum dose that would give a mouse protection. Not a control was alive at the end of twenty-four hours, while five of the treated mice were still alive at the end of three days.

Each of these experiments yielded important information. But the penicillin remained the main problem. It was so difficult to produce, there was so little available that the Professor was tremendously handicapped. However, another batch of the mould was harvested and extracted by the end of May.

"On June 1, by which time it was considered that enough penicillin would be available, Professor Florey arranged to carry out a large scale experiment with twenty-five mice as controls and fifty mice under treatment," said Dr. Jennings. "I started early in the morning to inject the seventy-five mice with half a cubic centimetre of a culture of *Streptococcus pyogenes*, and an hour afterwards Professor Florey started to inject fifty of the mice with doses of penicillin in order to try to arrive at the minimum dose that would save the mice. It was about 2.30 in the morning when Professor Florey gave the mice their last injection of penicillin, after giving them treatment for twelve hours. By this time ten of the controls were already dead and within two days the dead controls numbered seventeen, while forty-nine of the treated mice survived. Professor Florey determined to keep the mice under observation for ten days, the period he had fixed as the duration of the experiment, and at the end of this time twenty-five of the treated mice were still alive while twenty-one out of the twenty-five controls were dead. The value of penicillin as a therapeutic agent was evident—it was equally clear that Professor Florey had not treated the other mice with penicillin long enough to save them."

While Heatley was grappling with his problems, Professor Gardner was testing the effect of penicillin upon various germs to ensure that the previous findings by other scientists were accurate. His usual routine was to set up a series of test tubes, perhaps ten or a dozen in number, all seeded with the same germ on the medium suitable to them. To the first tube was added one drop of penicillin, to the second tube two drops, to the third tube, four drops, and so on, while one tube, the control, would receive no penicillin at all. The tubes were then placed in the incubator and allowed to remain growing for twenty-four hours, by which time the control tube would be cloudy with billions of germs, and little difference would be seen between it and the first four or five tubes, but the later ones in the series would be quite clear, showing that the penicillin had prevented the germs from growing. In this way Professor Gardner worked through a list of germs, adding one or two to the number which Fleming had found were susceptible to penicillin and one or two to those which remained unaffected.

In further work with Dr. R. C. Vollum he banished all hopes of using penicillin against tuberculosis. He was faced with two in-compatibles. On the one hand was the tubercle bacillus which developed so slowly that it needed fourteen days to grow a culture, and on the other was the penicillin which lost much of its potency in a few days. It seemed a physical impossibility to test the penicillin on the tubercle bacillus. But after much thought Professor Gardner hit on a workable plan—he determined to inject the germs in order to achieve the impossible. Perhaps it is not strictly accurate to state that he injected the germs—although I have watched a scientist inject some dye into a single white cell of the blood and I have little doubt that it would be possible to inject a single tubercle bacillus if it were necessary. What Professor Gardner did was to inject the culture tube with a fresh dose of penicillin every two days to main-tain the strength of the penicillin at the same level for fourteen days. It was a simple way out of a dilemma. Unhappily, the tubercle germs thrived in spite of the penicillin, and this effort of Professor Gardner proved that tuberculosis could never be cured with penicillin.

Another observation of the Oxford bacteriologist served to emphasize the extraordinary way in which penicillin acted and the peculiar things it could do. There was ample proof that it could prevent germs from growing, then quite unexpectedly he came on something in the white field of his microscope that was rather startling—evidence that penicillin could turn germs into giants. There was no doubt about it, for he saw that the germs which cause gas gangrene and the germs which cause typhoid fever had grown into monsters.

It was by sheer chance that he brought this about. He happened to administer a dose of penicillin to them which was not potent enough to kill them, but was too strong to enable them to grow and multiply in the normal fashion. They could not die, they could not live normally, but they continued to derive nourishment from their food and the consequence was that they grew into giant forms instead of splitting up and multiplying in the usual way.

I asked Professor Gardner how penicillin brought this about. "We don't know exactly," was the reply. "It disturbs the growth process and in some way prevents the division of each cell. We knew the process of cell division needs a high number of enzyme actions, and penicillin seems to act like a spanner in the works and throws the machinery out of gear."

"What happens to the giant germs?" I inquired.

"Most of them die off; but some of them survive and gradually assume normal size," was the reply.

It was when he tested penicillin upon the organisms which cause gas gangrene that Professor Gardner brought hope to many who were wounded in the war, for he found these organisms were sensitive to penicillin. At the time it was a laboratory experiment made in the test tube and nobody knew whether penicillin could be purified and stabilized; but if it could, the wounded would have a better chance than ever before.

Meanwhile Professor Florey and Dr. M. A. Jennings carried out experiments to discover the effects of penicillin upon mucus as well as the while cells of the body which play so big a part in overcoming disease. The various types of white cells, phagocytes, leucocytes, macrophages and others, are the scavengers of the human body; they seize on foreign substances in the blood stream or tissues and carry them off. One evening recently during a high wind something blew into my eye. It was very painful and my efforts to wash it out failed, so at bedtime I soaked a pad in boracic lotion, put it on my closed eye, donned an eye shade and went to sleep. Next morning there was a little spot of white matter in the inner corner of my eyelid and the eye was all right. When I examined this spot of matter under the glass, I saw wrapped up in it a tiny vegetable fibre finer than the sharpest needle about an eightieth of an inch long. My white cells had seized upon it, made a cushion of themselves all round it to prevent it from pricking my eye and had moved down with it to the corner where it could be removed. They engulf the germs of disease in the same way and digest them or deal with them to the best of their ability.

As we already know, Fleming and Reid had assured themselves that penicillin filtrate was harmless to the white cells, and Professor Florey not only wished to confirm these findings, but to compare the effect of penicillin on the white cells with the effect of some of the wonderful sulphonamide group of drugs such as sulphapyridine and sulphathiazole, along with proflavine and other drugs. As Dr. C. G. Paine had carried out tests with penicillin on the white cells, Florey made use of his technique and solution, although he varied the method of examining the cells. The white cells were suspended in a fluid consisting of distilled water in which seven different chemicals in varying proportions were dissolved with a little glucose and urea. The tests were heartening, for while the white cells tolerated the sulphonamides quite well, they tolerated the

penicillin even better, and it was found that no difference could be
detected between the white cells treated with one part of penicillin
in 500 of the test fluid and normal white cells that were not under
test at all. As penicillin affects staphylococci and streptococci in
dilutions of one part in a million, it was obvious that there was no
danger of using a dose of penicillin strong enough to kill off the
white cells before the germs were affected.

Meanwhile Britain's plight was desperate. The Home Guard
was mobilized. People all over the land were obliterating the names
of the towns in which they lived, blotting them out on railway
stations, on shop fronts, on vans, in telephone kiosks, to confuse the
German parachutists if they landed. The Home Office issued
millions of leaflets to tell people what to do in case of invasion. At
the height of this tense drama, Professor Florey knew at last that the
work he and his team of scientists were doing at Oxford would bear
fine fruit if it could be carried through to the end. The experiments
proved that penicillin was something wonderful. But at any moment
they might see German tanks come rumbling down the road at
Oxford, German soldiers might break into the laboratories and
destroy all they had worked for.

In that crisis the Oxford scientists were determined to save the
precious mould, if it were possible. One of them suggested a way.
"We can smear some of the mould on the linings of our jackets and
get it out of the country," he said. That was what they did. They
smeared the mould on the linings of their jackets and around the
insides of their inner pockets. It was unnoticeable.

If they could get out of the country they could easily isolate the
mould again from the spores in their pockets and start up fresh
cultures. They did not know how they would get out of the
country or where they would go, but they had ideas of reaching
Canada or America with the mould and continuing their work there.
Fortunately the Royal Air Force saved Great Britain from invasion
and so saved civilisation; but if the Germans had defiled the colleges
of Oxford, the scientists struggling to give the world penicillin were
prepared to take any risks to preserve their work.

Throughout these tense days of June Heatley worked strenuously
with his technical helpers to brew the penicillin while Abraham and
Chain concentrated on the chemical problems. They toiled through
the miracle week of Dunkirk, feeling an inner glow as the tale of the
rescued mounted day by day; they carried on quietly amid all the
alarms and rumours until the end of the month. By that time it was

expected to have enough penicillin for another big-scale experiment on mice, and in due course it was brought to Professor Florey.

There were fifty mice in their cages arranged on the benches when Dr. Jennings started to inject them at 8.46 on the morning of July 1. The dose was half a cubic centimetre containing between 350,000,000 and 450,000,000 virulent streptococci. So deadly was the dose that it seemed impossible for a mouse to survive, and it was as severe a test for penicillin as Professor Florey could devise. Just before ten o'clock he set aside twenty-five mice as controls and started to inject the others with penicillin. This time he was determined that the treated mice should have a sufficiency of penicillin, so he planned to treat them every three hours for forty-five hours, which meant that he had to remain in the laboratory for two nights and two days.

He slept on a concealed bed which closed up against the wall of his study, his technical assistant Mr. Kent slept on a camp bed in the next room. And every three hours the alarm clock brought them to their feet. "Are you ready, Kent?" the Professor said, and the two men concentrated on the task of injecting the twenty-five mice with penicillin. Then the records were made up, a drop of coffee was perhaps taken from a thermos flask, and the two would lie down again, to repeat the process three hours later.

"During the big experiments," Kent remarked, "we came back to the laboratory about seven o'clock from our evening meal to begin the night session. We used to find some of the controls with their coats standing up, looking a bit sick, and one or two would be dead, so I used to pick out the dead ones from the cages as the Professor made a note of them. Sometimes he would point to a mouse and say 'That looks a bit moribund', and a little later I would notice the mouse passing out. At other times he would come in and say 'How many more dead?', and I would give him the number."

In sixteen hours from the time the experiment started, the twenty-five controls were all dead, and twenty-four of the treated mice survived. It was proof enough for Professor Florey, who had never seen anything like it in his life. Picking up the telephone, he spoke to one of his team: "It looks like a miracle," he said.

Ten days later these twenty-four treated mice were still alive.

The proof was piling up, but before the Oxford scientists would permit themselves to make any announcement about penicillin they tested the drug against two other germs, *Staphylococcus aureus* and *Clostridium septique* and found, as they anticipated, that penicillin was effective against these germs. After further experiments on rats and cats to find out whether penicillin gave rise to any poisonous or injurious effects in the living body, the famous paper "Penicillin as a Chemotherapeutic Agent" was published in the *Lancet* of August 24, 1940. Here, at last, was an indication that the mystery of penicillin was being solved.

"It must be emphasized that the results of these preliminary tests have been obtained with an impure substance and such slight toxic effects as have been noted may possibly be due, in part at least, to these impurities," wrote the Oxford scientists, who summed up their work in these words: "The results are clear cut, and show that penicillin is active in *vivo* against at least three of the organisms inhibited in *vitro*. It would seem a reasonable hope that all organisms inhibited in high dilution in *vitro* will also be found to be dealt with in *vivo*. Penicillin does not appear to be related to any chemotherapeutic substance at present in use and is particularly remarkable for its activity against the anaerobic organisms associated with gas gangrene."

The comment of the *Lancet* was factual and sober. In touching on what had been done, it was careful to point out some of the things which had not been done. It suggested that penicillin had claims as a chemotherapeutic agent and concluded "what is its chemical nature and how it acts, and whether it can be prepared on a commercial scale, are problems to which the Oxford pathologists are doubtless addressing themselves."

They were.

CHAPTER IX

THE CHEMISTS TRIUMPH

BIGGER production and extraction became Heatley's task while Chain and his colleague Abraham concentrated their energies on the purification of the penicillin. With work going on in all departments at the same time, it is impossible to describe everything in its exact chronological order, as Professor Florey pointed out, so I will record the outstanding points in production and extraction before describing the chemical achievements of Chain and Abraham in purifying the penicillin.

More penicillin for experimental purposes meant growing more mould, making more medium, using more culture vessels and increasing the cultures. It entailed a big addition of work, but this particular work was tending to become routine, although it remained full of surprises and needed careful manipulation to prevent contamination and loss of penicillin.

It was the extraction which presented Heatley with the difficult problem. In the first place it was essential to make the filtered medium rather acid before the penicillin could be extracted with ether, and penicillin kept in this acidified state in the ordinary temperature of a room was prone to vanish into thin air before anything could be done to stop it. Now Heatley had no intention of producing penicillin in order to see it disappear in this way. Although it was more comfortable to work in the laboratory at ordinary temperatures, there were such things as refrigerated rooms in which it was possible to work at reduced temperatures—if necessary. But working at low temperatures induced discomfort, and frozen fingers were not conducive to delicate manipulation, so he concluded that by making the crude penicillin very cold, it should be possible to complete the extraction at room temperature before the fluid warmed up sufficiently to come to any harm. He was right.

Another drawback was not so easy to overcome. When the crude penicillin in this acid state was shaken up with ether to extract the penicillin from the medium and induce it to dissolve in the ether, a nasty scum was formed by the components of the medium. This tended to clog and choke the apparatus. However, one of the team suggested that if the mixture of crude penicillin and ether was rocked very gently, instead of being shaken vigorously, the scum might not be nearly so solid nor troublesome. It was another step forward.

Heatley's conception of the main method whereby the penicillin could be extracted was clever. He decided to try two or three well-known principles and combine them to achieve his end. One was the principle of water to run down hill. Then everyone knows that if oil be released under water, it will float to the top. Now when water is poured into a vessel containing oil, the water will sink to the bottom and the oil will rise to the surface. The movements of the two fluids are contrary, one rises while the other sinks, and they form a counter-current. Substitute ether for oil and you will see what Heatley proposed to do, he aimed to allow a current of crude penicillin to flow down a tube while a current of ether flowed up it. Both fluids would intermingle on the way and as the ether had a greater affinity for the penicillin than the penicillin had for the medium, the penicillin would dissolve in the ether and pass with it to the top of the tube instead of sinking with the watery medium to the bottom. By arranging a syphon at the top of a U-shaped tube with an outlet through which the ether and penicillin could flow into a container, and by arranging another syphon on the other tube with an outlet at the bottom through which the waste medium could escape, he could maintain his column of fluid in the tube at a constant height and allow the two currents of fluid to pass in opposite directions, and thus extract the penicillin automatically.

The theory was sound, but it was by no means easy to carry out. He juggled with big glass tubes and little glass tubes and bits of rubber tubing, using the Bunsen flame on his bench with the skill of an experienced glass-blower as he struggled to make the first apparatus for extracting the penicillin. He did it all himself, with the exception of a great spiral glass tube which was supplied commercially. He was his own mechanic, electrician, carpenter—jack of all trades. He could not only use his brain, but his hands, and he had the ability to invent things to do what he wanted as he went along. When his efforts were completed he stood before a flattened glass tube three-eighths of an inch in diameter and fifteen feet long that formed a spiral from the top of which he planned to release his crude penicillin while the ether flowed in at the bottom. As penicillin in this acid form was very unstable at room temperature, he arranged to add the acid to the crude penicillin at the very entrance to the extraction tube, give the fluids a chance to blend in a short mixing chamber and then allow them to flow down the tube. In this way he reduced the time that the penicillin was in its acidified state to the few seconds that it was actually passing down the extraction tube.

Two other inherent difficulties faced him. One was the tendency of the acidified penicillin and ether to blend together and form a true emulsion from which it was hard to extract the penicillin afterwards; the other was the tendency of the mixture to form an intractable scum.

Starting his apparatus working, he soon saw that there was no danger of forming an emulsion, for the crude penicillin flowed in a stream which did not break up into drops at all. But a nasty scum formed where the ether and the penicillin met. When in addition his tests proved that a good deal of the penicillin was being lost because the crude penicillin did not mix sufficiently with the ether, he calmly abandoned the apparatus and tried again.

This time he stretched a number of cotton threads down which the crude penicillin could flow in a tube full of ether. It worked up to a point. But it was not good enough. Too much penicillin was still lost. And the cotton threads tended to choke at the top with matter precipitated from the medium, thus interrupting the free flow of crude penicillin down the cotton threads almost as effectively as though the choked threads were a number of choked pipes.

Then he tested the theory of allowing the crude penicillin to fall down through the ether in the form of small droplets, and found it was possible to extract a high percentage of penicillin. Drops that were too big ran together and defeated his aim; drops that were too small sank too slowly and flooded the machine. It was essential to use drops of exactly the right size, neither too small, nor too large.

To obtain the correct drops, he made glass jets of various types one after the other; he tried metal jets to give the spray he needed, but none was efficient. In the end he softened a holder of glass in the bunsen flame and pushed a needle right home until only a fraction of the point was exposed and with this he pierced a platinum disc with a series of holes at certain intervals. By punching the needle through as far as possible, he ensured that the holes were identical in size.

When the crude penicillin dripped through this platinum disc, the extraction of penicillin was fairly high; and although a scum formed at the bottom of the tube, it now broke up into little bits and floated away with the waste fluid of the medium.

Here, after many a setback and disappointment, were the main principles on which the first automatic apparatus was based, a method which promised good extraction and a way of overcoming the difficulty of the scum. The apparatus which Dr. Heatley constructed consisted of six extraction tubes mounted in an oak case. I hoped that this historic penicillin plant would ultimately find a place in South Kensington Museum with our other national treasures, but unfortunately on my first visit to Oxford I found that it had been almost completely dismantled and the parts used to make other apparatus.

Though difficult to work out, the method can be stated simply enough to be understood by all. The extraction tubes were fed by three one-gallon bottles. One contained the ether, a second contained the crude penicillin, and the third contained the acid for mixing with the latter. The bottles were inverted in a rack at the top of the apparatus, and to enable the bottles to be turned upside down without spilling the contents, Heatley invented a special bung which closed the bottle until it was in position, then a slight pressure to lock the bottle home pushed aside a glass ball closing the bung and enabled the liquid to flow into the feeding pipes until the bottles were empty. To ensure that full bottles were always ready to replace the empty ones, a system of signals was arranged so that when the liquid in the bottles reached a certain level it operated electrical contacts which rang a bell and switched on a red light to attract attention.

The ether could be used over and over again, but some of it naturally became mixed with the waste fluids and went down the drain. To rid the remaining ether of water, it was necessary to distil it and Heatley made his still out of an ordinary zinc dustbin which he heated with steam. The ether was, of course, inflammable and there was always the danger that it would ignite and cause a fire. In addition it was very volatile and evaporated easily, so it was not only dangerous, but rather costly to use. But so long as ether was the only solvent known to be capable of extracting penicillin, it was used, every care being taken to avoid risks of fire and to lessen the losses by evaporation.

Then one day, Dr. Chain remarked: "Why not use amyl acetate instead of ether?"

That marked another step in the production of penicillin. Amyl acetate worked even better than ether and thereafter the air around the extraction apparatus was redolent with the flavour of old-fashioned pear drops.

"It was a big improvement," Dr. Heatley remarked.

There was less risk of fire. And as amyl acetate was a heavier liquid than ether, the drops of crude penicillin sank through it more slowly with the result that the amyl acetate was able to extract more of the precious drug from the medium. The great disadvantage of amyl acetate was that it caused such a heavy scum that the second part of the process had to be modified. In this way, by trial and error, the difficulties were gradually overcome and toward the end of 1940 Heatley succeeded in working out the method of extracting penicillin automatically.

A number of girls who became known as the Penicillin Girls played their part in production. Sometimes they worked in the refrigeration chamber where, clad in thick coats and mufflers, they took the big bottles of medium and ether and rolled them gently up and down on their knees several times to extract the penicillin into the ether. One of the girls used to stand up and rock the bottles in her outstretched hands because she preferred to do it that way. And Dr. Heatley, who did much of the early work in the refrigerator, was once seen standing on the roof, wrapped up in overcoat and scarf, his hands encased in warm gloves, with the snow lying thick all round him as he rocked the great bottles to extract the penicillin in the cold air during a special test on temperature.

It was not easy to find the best type of vessel in which to grow the mould, and Heatley tested one thing after another. Glass bottles of many different shapes and sizes were tried; he used baking tins covered with cellophane to prevent the mould from becoming contaminated by airborne bacteria, but too much medium was lost by evaporation; he even experimented with flat bed pans and for one test he fell back upon ordinary half-size biscuit tins found in the grocer's shop, adapting them for his purpose by soldering spouts to them and trying to lacquer them. Unfortunately all the trouble spent on the biscuit tins was wasted owing to the stripping of the lacquer in the autoclave and the chemical action of the medium upon the tin.

In the end he designed an oblong porcelain vessel, rough outside so that it would not slip about and glazed inside so that it could easily be cleaned and sterilized, with a spout through which it could be filled sticking up at an angle at one end. It was roughly ten and a half inches long, eight and a half inches wide and two and a half inches deep, and it could be packed closely on the shelves of the incubator and in the autoclaves.

With everyone in the country concentrating on war work to rearm the British Army that had escaped from Dunkirk, there

seemed to be little prospect of getting these vessels made until the
war was over. Drawing one or two rough sketches, Heatley wrote a
letter or two and was pleased to hear that Messrs. J. Macintyre and
Co. were prepared to make sample vessels and produce them in
quantity if they proved satisfactory. The potters knew their craft.
They made the exact thing that was wanted, whereupon Heatley
rushed up to Burslem in Staffordshire to see Mr. Ernest Watkins
about the order. At first glance the buildings looked old-fashioned
and there was an atmosphere about the place that carried memories
of the spacious past when things moved at a saner pace than that of
to-day; but never was anything more deceptive, for underlying the
quietness was a knowledge of the potter's craft and an efficiency and
drive that could not be bettered. The potters knew there was a war
on. They did not labour the point. The scientists in Oxford were
conducting their own war and Mr. Watkins was anxious to help.
He found out what was wanted, consulted one or two members of
the staff, and in three weeks notified Dr. Heatley that the first batch
of special vessels was ready.

Borrowing a motor-van in Oxford, Heatley drove it up to
Staffordshire on December 22, 1940. The day was cold, but the roads
were dry and he drew into the potter's yard in the late afternoon to
see about loading. "Leave it to us," they said. "We'll attend to that."

They did. When Heatley called in the morning he found the van
packed and waiting for him. Getting into the driver's seat, he drove
back to Oxford. Wasting no time, he got the van unpacked, and
on December 24 he was helped by Mr. G. Glister to charge the
vessels with medium before putting them into the autoclave
to sterilize them. And on Christmas Day, 1940, he went to his
laboratory early and seeded seventy-six of the vessels with the
spores of the mould. It was a long and tiring task, but the work he
did in his laboratory that Christmas Day bore fine fruit.

These were the culture vessels upon which Professor Florey
depended to grow sufficient mould to give him the penicillin for a
clinical test. They were the first of several batches of vessels that the
potters made for the Oxford scientists. Incidentally the same potters
made the little porcelain tubes with which Heatley assayed the
potency of the penicillin.

Although the introduction of a yeast extract into the medium
had cut down the period of growth to about seven days, this still
seemed a long time to wait for the small quantity of penicillin that
was produced. Heatley worried at experiments to try to cut down

OPPOSITE: *Dr. Norman G. Heatley, the Oxford scientist, who designed and
made the first apparatus for extracting penicillin and who solved important
problems of growing the mould which produces penicillin. His first extraction
apparatus is shown overleaf.*

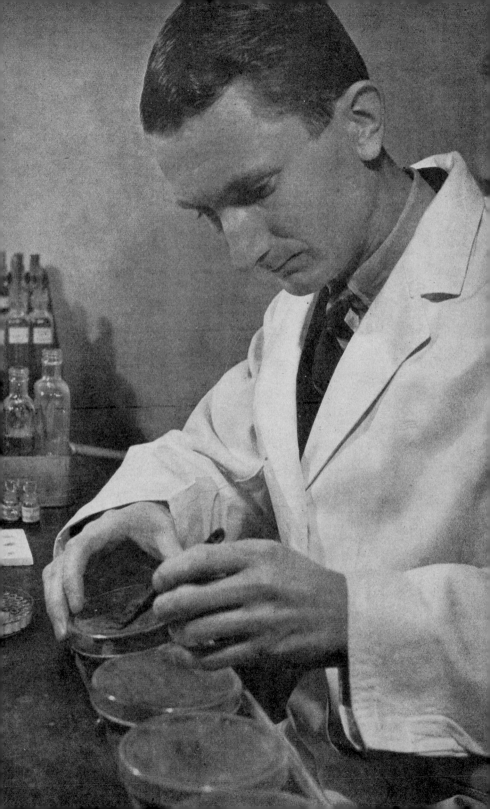

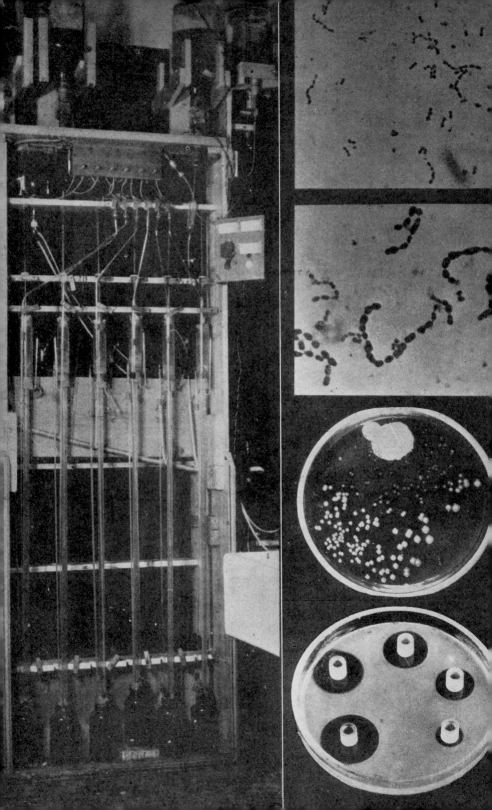

the time still more. The mould was producing its greatest yield after growing for about seven days. There were several days wasted when the mould was simply making growth and yielding no penicillin at all. Was it possible for the mould to produce a second crop of penicillin? If so, could he withdraw the medium and introduce a new lot of medium? These were questions that could be answered only by actual tests.

Heatley turned over the problem in his mind. The mould grew on the surface of the medium and if the medium were withdrawn, the mould would drop to the bottom of the vessel and break in many places. After such a disturbance the mould might take several days to recover and waste the very time it was designed to save. The risk of contamination was also considerable.

To overcome these drawbacks, he invented a method of introducing sterile compressed air while drawing off the medium, and as the new medium flowed in, it expelled the compressed air. It was an ingenious method, and Heatley found that its adoption enabled him to harvest a second yield of penicillin in three days. This was a great saving in time. In one case the medium was changed fourteen times and the mould produced fifteen crops of penicillin. Yet the method had drawbacks, and eventually it was abandoned for the old way of seeding the medium afresh each time.

During these months of 1940 the main efforts of Heatley and his technical assistants were centred on obtaining enough penicillin to treat human beings so that Professor Florey could carry out the first clinical tests. No member of the team engaged on the work at Oxford had reason to doubt the results. The experiments on mice pointed to the successful treatment of men.

Meanwhile Dr. Chain and Dr. Abraham in the biochemical department worked continuously on the difficult chemical problems of concentration and purification. Their great aim was to isolate the pure penicillin and no men ever faced a more discouraging task.

As the work and the problems piled up, each member of the team drew on his store of scientific knowledge to further the main aim which was to provide proof, if they could, that penicillin was an effective agent for the treatment of human diseases. They pulled together, as a good team will; they discussed their problems at lunch or over a cup of tea; they worked far into the night and often took meals in the laboratory to avoid wasting time in going out. While the Royal Air Force fought the Battle of Britain in the air,

G—m

OPPOSITE: *The first penicillin extraction apparatus made by Dr. N. G. Heatley. On the right at top are normal streptococci, magnified 1,000 times, changed into giant forms below by penicillin; next is Fleming's original plate with colonies of germs dissolving round the patch of mould at top; the last shows Heatley's potency test with the plate white with germs except around the cylinders containing the penicillin.*

they fought their war against germs in the laboratories of Oxford.

All of them knew that penicillin was a remarkable chemotherapeutic substance. None knew better than Dr. Chain and Dr. Abraham how elusive it was. In their efforts to purify the drug the two chemists toiled like the alchemists of olden days to make their chemcal brews, tiny potions to blend with the drop of brown liquid containing the infinitesimal fraction of penicillin. At times it seemed impossible for them to touch penicillin without destroying it. They watched chemical reaction follow chemical reaction without yielding any positive results.

Methodically Chain and Abraham sought to purify the substance by precipitating it in the form of a salt, so they added a preparation of zinc to the penicillin fluid in the hope of bringing this about, but the penicillin vanished. They tried copper with the same result. Cadmium, mercury, lead and nickel were all tried and found useless; each in its turn destroyed the potency of penicillin. They even tried to use the power of uranium to materialize the magic of penicillin, but the metal which destroyed Hiroshima was equally deadly to the drug. Then they experimented with many of the known chemical bases in the hope that penicillin would enter into combination and form an insoluble salt. Quinine, cinchonine and cinchonidine, acridine and proflavine—all were useless. Defeated in this direction, they turned to various ketones and alcohols—in vain. They invented variations of known methods with negative results, yet although failure followed failure they continued their search with zeal. Occasionally Professor Florey dropped in to learn progress and encourage them with his own determination and optimism.

As they tried one chemical reaction after another, the possibilities left to them became more and more restricted. Already they had tried to purify penicillin by adopting the method of chromatography with water, but it would not work. They tried other methods and were repeatedly baffled. Then into the mind of the younger chemist came the thought that although chromatography had not worked with water, there was a chance that it might work with ether. Discussing the problem, Chain and Abraham decided to try chromatography once more, and this time to use ether instead of water. To their delight the process worked, the luck ran in their favour and they had the satisfaction of stripping the brown extract of penicillin of most of its impurities and obtaining a purer form of penicillin than ever before.

A broad outline without confusing details may enable readers to understand how they accomplished this well-nigh insuperable task. What they did was to take a glass tube, three feet in length and three inches in diameter, and fill it with Brockman alumina. This was a fine white powder resembling ground rice or table salt, and it ran as easily as table salt or silver sand. When moistened, it cohered, or stuck together just as the fine sand of the seashore coheres to stand up in a solid mass when the children make their sand pies. Into the glass tube they poured their concentrated solution of ether and penicillin which was a red-brown fluid full of impurities. The powdered alumina separated out the various substances in the liquid in a magical way. The substances for which the powder had the greatest affinity were caught at the top of the column and held fast in a band of brown colour; beneath this band another of a light yellow colour was formed and into this band went practically all the penicillin, below this was formed a dark brown band of impurities and below this at the bottom of the column was a purple band containing more impurities.

Locked up, somewhere with the alumina powder in the glass tube was the penicillin. A test soon disclosed that the top band contained very little penicillin, so it was carefully removed with a metal spatula and discarded. A test of the second band showed that it contained about eighty per cent of the penicillin; the next band had only a faint trace of penicillin and the bottom band contained none at all. The band containing the penicillin was defined by the alteration in colour as clearly as though it were marked with a pencil, and it was an easy matter for the chemists to remove the unwanted band above it and scrape out the band of alumina containing the drug. Naturally they took precautions to test the margins slightly above and slightly below this band to recover any traces of penicillin that had overlapped the normal zone in which the drug was deposited.

That was the way in which the chromatographic method operated to separate penicillin from many of its impurities by filtering the penicillin fluid through powdered alumina. As this penicillin fluid had already been partly purified, a few notes on the earlier processes will help to a better understanding of what Chain and Abraham accomplished. Taking the crude penicillin fluid after it had been separated from the mould, they cooled the liquid in the refrigerator until it was just above freezing point, about thirty-nine degrees Fahrenheit, when they acidified it with phosphoric acid. Their first aim was to separate the penicillin from the various chemicals in the medium, so they shook up the fluid with an equal quantity of amyl acetate into which practically all the penicillin passed. From now on they sought to banish the impurities and to concentrate the penicillin by lessening the amount of fluid with which it was mixed. As the salt of penicillin has a greater affinity for water than for amyl acetate, they added one litre of water to two litres of amyl acetate and shook them together, while adding an alkali to reduce the acidity, whereupon the penicillin flowed out of the amyl acetate into the water. When the two fluids had settled into distinct layers, the penicillin and water were drawn off and used once more to recover the penicillin from another two litres of amyl acetate. In this way the same water containing an increasing quantity of penicillin was used ten times to recover the penicillin from twenty litres of amyl acetate, so the same amount of penicillin as was previously dissolved in twenty litres of amyl acetate was concentrated in one litre of water of a deep red-brown colour and in the process quite a lot of impurities were left behind in the amyl acetate.

The penicillin solution was then filtered and passed through powdered bone charcoal to remove further impurities before it was cooled to forty degrees Fahrenheit to be mixed with a third of the quantity of cold ether. The ether formed a layer on top of the red-brown penicillin fluid which was acidified, to enable it to combine with the ether. This ether containing a high proportion of the penicillin was then drawn off, and a similar quantity of fresh ether was added to the penicillin fluid to draw off more penicillin, after which a third amount of ether was added to draw off as much as possible of the remaining penicillin. The litre of penicillin and water had now been changed to a litre of penicillin and ether, and it was this fluid which was poured through the powdered alumina in the glass tube as previously described.

All the penicillin was washed out of the alumina by shaking it up with a phosphate buffer fluid that was neither acid nor alkali. The alumina was washed four times to extract the penicillin which was thus transferred into six litres of fluid. These four washings took seven and a half hours.

Again the chemists cooled this fluid and made it acid so that as much penicillin as possible could flow back into one-third of the quantity of ether. They repeated this operation three times with fresh supplies of ether, and then condensed the volume by adding alkali to make the mixture less acid and transferring the penicillin to one fifth of the quantity of water. It left a good deal of pigment behind in the ether.

Pressing on with the purification, they passed the penicillin back into a similar quantity of ether, which they filtered through another glass tube ten inches long and an inch in diameter, containing powdered alumina. This time the penicillin occupied about half the length of the tube. Washing out the penicillin from the alumina with phosphate buffer, they recovered it from the buffer with ether before transferring it to water again. At this stage they were able by a process of evaporation to obtain a light yellow powder which was a barium salt of penicillin mixed with pigment.

By now they were making real progress, but their task was by no means finished. Gradually each operation had reduced the impurities and left the penicillin in a purer form. Yet impurities still remained, so by further manipulations they managed to precipitate the yellow pigment and then concentrate the penicillin as a solution of barium salt in water.

This barium salt of penicillin dissolved in water was extracted once more with amyl acetate in the usual way and filtered for the third time through an alumina column. This time the column was divided into three zones. On top was a narrow, light brown zone, below it was an off-white zone twelve times as deep containing the penicillin, and below that a narrow zone of greenish yellow. When viewed under ultra-violet light, the top and bottom zones glowed with fluorescence like uranium. Twice more the penicillin was extracted and passed through the alumina column before Chain and Abraham were content with the degree of purity achieved.

Starting with crude material that contained only half a unit of penicillin, they had slowly and laboriously concentrated and purified it until they obtained between seventy and one hundred units per milligramme after passing through the first alumina column; by the time it emerged from the fifth alumina column and was ready for drying they had secured a concentration of between 450 and 500 units per milligramme. This was a fine accomplishment.

There remained the problem of evaporating the water to obtain the penicillin in powder form. Most people evaporate water by putting it in a kettle upon the fire or gas until it boils away in the form of steam, which is also a gas. So used are we to this method that we imagine it is impossible to boil away all the water in a kettle unless we make it very hot to generate steam. But the boiling point, otherwise the evaporation or distillation point, of water depends upon the pressure of the air. It is the pressure of the air lying on top of the water like a solid block of iron weighing about fifteen pounds to the square inch which prevents it from bubbling away so rapidly in the form of steam. The kettle of water which takes such a long time and such a lot of heat to boil at sea level will boil amazingly quickly with little heat at the top of Mount Everest.

It was impossible for the scientists to evaporate the water from the penicillin fluid by boiling it, because the heat would have destroyed the penicillin. But they knew it was a common fallacy to imagine that the only way of evaporating water was to heat it up until it steamed away. They were able to evaporate water just as well by going to the other extreme and using a high vacuum with intense cold. This is what they did. They placed the watery solution of penicillin in a special flask connected with a high vacuum pump and between the flask and the air pump they arranged a drain to act as a trap for the water. They packed this water-trap in acetone and solid carbon dioxide—the latter is the glistening white chemical used by the men who sell ices in the street to prevent their ices from melting—and with this mixture they forced the temperature of the flask down until it was ninety degrees Fahrenheit below zero. In this bitter cold under a high vacuum the water was quickly evaporated and sucked away from the penicillin by the suction pump, to be caught on the way in the trap where it remained frozen while the precious penicillin freed of all moisture was left frozen to the walls of the flask, from which it was scraped in the form of a dry smooth yellow powder that resembled wheaten flour to the touch.

That powder was a triumph for Chain and Abraham. Nothing like it was ever seen in the world before, and they had some justification for thinking that they had solved their major chemical problems and overcome their greatest difficulties and that it might now be a comparatively simple matter to crystallize the barium salt of penicillin. They little knew that this wonderful product of a lowly mould concealed a few more mysteries to intrigue and baffle the scientists.

This dry yellow powder which they scraped from the flask seemed too good to be true, for Professor Florey discovered during the course of his biological tests that one part mixed with twenty-four million parts of medium and one part mixed with thirty million parts of medium sufficed to prevent the test staphylococcus from growing. It was phenomenal. Its potency was so great that Professor Florey and his colleagues could scarcely believe it.

Still more astounding was the fact that this barium salt of penicillin was even then only half pure.

CHAPTER X

FLOREY SEEKS AMERICAN AID

As we know, Heatley, Chain and Abraham, with their technical assistants, worked hard throughout 1940 to secure enough penicillin for Professor Florey to make a test on human beings. All the laboratory tests pointed to success. Harmless to white cells and to living mice and rabbits and cats, penicillin had proved its power of saving mice that were inoculated with the germs of death. The drug was soluble to an extraordinary degree and diffused freely. The effect of this was that it made its way fairly quickly through the fluids of the body to the kidneys, and within an hour or so a good deal of the injected penicillin passed out of the body in the urine from which much of it could be recovered apparently unchanged and without showing any loss of activity. This action of penicillin enabled it to be used twice. It was another remarkable attribute of this unique drug. But on the other hand it could not be taken by mouth because the gastric juices soon destroyed it. This was a great drawback.

It was not possible to treat a case of generalized septicæmia, or blood poisoning, with a single massive dose of penicillin. In the first place there was too little of the drug available. Nor would it remain long enough in the body to overcome the germs, for a large part of it would flow to the kidneys and out of the body before it had a chance of exercising its power against the invaders. Yet to do any good, it was essential to keep a certain amount of penicillin circulating in the blood stream so that it could exert its beneficent effects all the time and aid the white cells and body fluids to overcome the infection. One way of accomplishing this was obviously by frequent injections made directly the amount of penicillin in the blood began to drop below a certain level, or else by adopting the method of allowing the penicillin to drip into a vein continuously, as in a blood transfusion.

There was the vexed question of the size of the dose to be administered. It was not a question of how much to give, but how little. The quantity that the Oxford workers were gathering was so trifling that there was not a speck to spare. It was too precious to waste a trace. Under the most favourable conditions, even if ample supplies

of penicillin had been available, the first treatment of a human being
was bound to be fraught with anxiety. The drug had cured mice,
but mice were not men. Would it act as harmlessly and effectively
in men as in mice? There was good reason to think so. Yet it did
not act in exactly the same way upon rabbits as it did upon cats and
mice. There was the doubt. Would man prove different? Nothing
but an actual test could tell. And upon the strength of the doses
which saved the mice, Professor Florey and the physicians had to
work out the correct dosage for human beings. And they had to be
small doses, as small as was possible without making them ineffective.

The paucity of penicillin was the main problem. Penicillin itself
was the key to the rest. Without it they could do little. With it they
might do anything. Baulked by the lack of the drug, and determined
to do everything possible to obtain it, Professor Florey left the quiet
precincts of the colleges and went out in the autumn of 1940 to enlist
the co-operation of a chemical firm and explain what they were doing
at Oxford.

"Look here, this looks good stuff," he said. "What we need is
enough to try out on a man. Will you help us? You can produce it in
this way."

He explained the method of production. They listened cour-
teously. The biological difficulties were not easily brushed aside.
The war pressed hardly upon their staff and plant. They were fully
extended.

"We will do our best," they said.

At the end of three months, when nothing was forthcoming,
Florey said to his colleagues: "We shall have to make it for
ourselves."

So the first British chemical firm were unable to meet Florey's
request to make the most wonderful chemotherapeutic substance
ever discovered in medical history. In justice it must be said that
they had excellent reasons. Their entire staff and plant were indeed
working night and day on war contracts.

They may also have been profoundly influenced by another factor.
Their wide technical knowledge told them of so many natural
products which had been synthesized. It seemed only yesterday
that no chemist knew anything of Vitamin C. Now it could be
bought in the shops for a few shillings a hundred tablets. The intricate technical process of growing the mould and extracting and
purifying the penicillin was a task bordering on the superhuman.
Chemists who studied the technique and saw how far Chain and

Abraham had succeeded were likely to believe that penicillin would soon be obtained in a pure form, and it would not be long before its exact chemical constitution was determined and it could be made synthetically in the laboratory.

There was the risk. They might spend an immense fortune on plant to obtain penicillin from the mould in the natural way and directly their apparatus was complete they might be faced with the fact that penicillin had been synthesized. At one stroke all their money might be lost, the plant on which they had spent a fortune might be obsolete, and they might be able to make penicillin from certain chemicals in the laboratory at a tenth of the cost of growing the mould. The mere possibility of being able to make penicillin synthetically was bound to have a hampering effect.

All the factories making penicillin in the world to-day run this risk of being made obsolete overnight by the announcement that penicillin has been synthesized in the laboratory. It will depend on the cost. If it costs more to make penicillin synthetically than it does to produce it in the natural way from the growing mould, we may be sure that the synthetic process will be confined to a few laboratory experiments and the penicillin manufacturers need have no further fears of their plant becoming worthless.

Florey had much to do and more to think about while Heatley, Chain and Abraham were slowly adding to the penicillin stored in the refrigerator. It seemed such a minute quantity. No one looking at it could imagine that countless lives depended on it, no one except these men whose faith in it was absolute. They had seen with their own eyes what it could do for mice. But Professor Florey, being a scientist, could not say what would be its effect on man. He had to inject it to find out.

In the first days of 1941 Heatley and his assistants harvested the first brew of penicillin from the new culture vessels he had devised, and from then on they toiled to produce and extract a hundred litres of penicillin filtrate a week. By the beginning of February the reserve of penicillin was still pitifully small, yet Florey felt justified in risking it all upon one desperate case.

The previous October a policeman was admitted into the Radcliffe Infirmary, Oxford, where he lay under the care of Dr. C. M. Fletcher. Early in September the constable had noticed a small sore at the corner of his mouth, and by October 12th he was obliged to go into Hospital suffering from generalized blood poisoning, caused by a mixed infection of *Staphylococcus aureus* and *Streptococcus pyogenes* both of which were susceptible to penicillin.

The physicians treated him for a week with sulphapyridine until he developed a rash arising from the drug, but his condition did not improve. They operated on the abscesses to let out the pus in the hope that it would turn the scale, but their hopes were vain. They operated on his eyes, they gave him a blood transfusion, but he grew steadily worse and lost more and more weight. The infection spread to his lungs. He was a dying man, coughing up myriads of the germs that were killing him. All that medical science could do, all that care and attention and expert nursing could do, was done for him, without avail.

Upon this hopeless case it was decided to expend all the penicillin in existence. It was a very severe test of the curative value of the drug. Accordingly on February 12, 1941, the physicians in charge of the case administered 200 milligrames of the drug into a vein so that it might enter the blood stream and circulate all over the body. The doctors watched the patient carefully. There was a faint shiver, which was found to be caused by an impurity that was later eliminated, but there was no ill-effect. Then every three hours they injected another 100 milligrammes.

By the end of twenty-four hours the transformation was amazing. The sober, factual report of the case goes so far as to say: "Striking improvement after total of 800 mg. penicillin in twenty-four hours." The wounds on the patient's head ceased to discharge, the right eye ceased to run, there was every evidence that the constable had taken a turn towards recovery. On February 13 he received injections every four hours of 100 milligrammes of penicillin. Next day he was given a blood transfusion and penicillin was administered every two hours through the same drip tube, a total of one gramme being given during the twenty-four hours.

By now they were getting woefully short of penicillin. Some of the drug, however, was excreted in the urine which was treated to recover the penicillin it contained. This penicillin was quite unchanged by its passage through the body; no chemical reaction had occurred in it; in its own way it was as active as the new penicillin that Heatley was striving so desperately to produce. The recovered penicillin was used a second time on February 15. Next day the patient was much improved; but the penicillin was getting so scarce that for six hours there was none to administer.

The mould had to be grown before the penicillin could be harvested. It was like wheat, it needed a certain time to mature. Heatley did his best to expedite the growth of the mould and the extraction of the drug; but he could not conjure up penicillin from nowhere.

It was now fairly plain that sufficient penicillin would probably save the constable's life; it was equally plain that in a few hours all the penicillin would be used up. It was a tragic position. In five days they had given the patient nearly four and a half grammes of penicillin. The patient felt better, he was eating better, his fever was gone, the sores on his face and head were healing. The deadly germs were being vanquished.

Unhappily he could not maintain the improvement without the penicillin. For about ten days he held the balance, then the germs began to get the upper hand and on March 15 he died. Florey, the scientist who dealt with facts, wrote a factual report of "this forlorn case" which showed such a striking change for the better after being treated with penicillin. But there were two blood transfusions to be taken into account and he did not know whether these had brought about the improvement.

But Florey felt sure that if he had possessed enough penicillin he could have saved the constable's life. To-day he knows it to be true. But he had no definite proof then. He was sad at the death of the patient. "The Professor was very upset over it," Mr. James Kent remarked.

"We take no more cases until we have got enough stuff to carry them through," was the Professor's decision.

The second case was a boy of fifteen with a hip wound infected with *haemolytic streptococcus*—another germ sensitive to penicillin. This case did not end so unfortunately and Professor Florey was able to sum it up: "Penicillin therapy was followed by a great improvement in the patient's general condition, in spite of the dose being insufficient to maintain a detectable concentration of penicillin continuously in the blood."

The rapid way in which penicillin escaped from the body presented a most difficult problem. To maintain an adequate amount of penicillin in the blood stream to fight an infection was, as Florey once graphically put it, "like trying to fill a bath with the plug out."

By May 3 the treatment of the third patient was begun with 200 milligrammes of penicillin being allowed to drip into a vein continuously every hour. At the end of five hours, when one gramme of the drug had been given, the dose was reduced to 100 milligrammes an hour and in four days a great carbuncle four inches across was healing nicely and in twelve days the patient was discharged from hospital. It was a clear-cut success of the penicillin over the *Staphy-lococcus aureus*, for this large carbuncle was absorbed without discharging or causing a scar.

On May 13 penicillin was administered to a little boy of four and a half years old who was so ill that he was only half conscious. In three days the boy was "obviously better" and in a week he was talking and playing with his toys, and in thirteen days his general condition was pronounced excellent. It seemed practically certain that he would soon be quite well again when he ruptured a blood vessel and passed away. To lose a patient in this way through an accident was discouraging.

Out of four patients treated with penicillin, two had died and these bald facts would not suggest to ordinary people that penicillin was very effective. But in this last case it was possible to obtain direct evidence of the remarkable way in which the penicillin had hastened the healing in the child's lungs and other infected places. Far from being unfavourable, the evidence was building up in the most favourable manner, and by the time that Dr. Fletcher had treated two more cases and dealt with four eye cases, the hope of penicillin being a wonderful drug was generally confirmed.

The Oxford team who overcame the difficulties of producing and purifying penicillin published an account of their work under their joint names in the *Lancet*, stating that "in all cases a favourable therapeutic response was obtained." They summed up their scientific opinion in a few words: "Enough evidence, we consider, has now been assembled to show that penicillin is a new and effective type of chemotherapeutic agent, and possesses some properties unknown in any antibacterial substance hitherto described."

It might be thought that this evidence would have been sufficient to start the Governments of the world producing penicillin. But it did no such thing. Penicillin was almost as far removed from mankind as ever. Its powers were proved, but it did not exist except for a tiny quantity stored in the refrigerator of the School of Pathology at Oxford. Let it be remembered that the war dominated everything and everyone. In all classes people who could work were making munitions or helping the war effort in other ways. Nightly the German bombers did their best to destroy Britain's houses and factories. The slaughter of men, women and innocent children went on remorselessly. No man in the south of England who left his home for work in the morning knew if he would live to return at night. And no family sleeping in their homes knew if they would live to see the light of another day. Anywhere, everywhere, death might fall upon them out of the skies at any instant.

In these conditions the nation carried on the daily task. Mr. Winston Churchill and the British Government were far too busy saving the British nation and the rest of Civilization to seek additional responsibilities. If the Ministry of Health noted what Florey and his colleagues had done, they sent no intimation to the School of Pathology at Oxford University, nor did they offer to finance the further production of penicillin. With the publication of the evidence, some of the most important chemical firms in England made inquiries at Oxford for technical information, and their chemists began to carry out researches envisaging the ultimate big-scale production of penicillin. But although the Oxford team had found a way of solving many problems, the scientists in the commercial laboratories were compelled to work out their own varying techniques, a procedure that took time.

Realizing at last that there was no immediate prospect of any firm in England producing enough penicillin to carry out the extensive clinical trials that were necessary, and knowing the urgency of the matter, Florey turned to America. The United States were not at war. There was no danger of German bombs destroying American factories. The Rockefeller Foundation had already co-operated by paying part of the cost of the penicillin researches and it gladly agreed to defray the travelling expenses when it learned that Florey would like to visit the United States to see if he could further the work and arrange for penicillin to be produced for tests on a wider scale. This was how it came about that Professor Florey and Dr. Heatley found themselves in Lisbon on June 27, 1941, with a supply of mould in their baggage, waiting for the Clipper to fly them to the United States. The weather was torrid and the scientists could not help imagining what would be its effect on the mould. After enduring three hot days in Lisbon, they boarded the Clipper, tucked their pyjamas and tooth brushes in the little blue and white linen bags provided for the purpose, watched their baggage being sent down below and then settled down in their cosy seats.

In under seven hours they dropped down at Horta in the Azores where they had tea. The aircraft refuelled and their bunks were made up. As they sped westward to Bermuda they donned their pyjamas and turned in for the night. Early next morning they came to Bermuda and by the time they arrived in New York on July 2 Heatley noted with misgivings that the temperature was ninety-two degrees Fahrenheit in the shade. He was worried about the mould. He could not help wondering if it would survive the high temperature, for *Penicillium notatum* had proved by bitter experience that it was not the sort of mould with which to take liberties.

Next day they went to stay with a scientific friend of Professor Florey to the north of New York, and during the following four days, which were charged with the added excitement of Independence Day celebrations on July 4, they discussed their project with their host, whose advice and help proved to be invaluable. "I'll take you along to Ross Harrison of the National Research Council," he said.

He did. Ross Harrison listened patiently until he heard that they were interested in a mould. "The man to see is Thom," he advised.

Accordingly they rang up the famous American mycologist to make an appointment. "If you can be ready at 7.50 to-morrow morning, I'll call for you," said Dr. Thom.

They rose early, took breakfast, and promptly to the minute a car rushed up to the hotel and Dr. Thom jumped out and greeted them. He was elderly, with a rugged, clean-shaven face, carried himself very straight and had decided opinions of his own. He soon ushered them into the car and whisked them off to the Bureau of Plant Industry at Beltsville where he showed them round and learned what they were about. "I think you should go to Coghill at Peoria," said Dr. Thom. "I'll take you in to see Wells at Washington."

Accordingly he took the two British scientists to the United States Department of Agriculture in Washington where he introduced them to Dr. Wells. "I'll wire May in Peoria to help you all he can," said Dr. Wells.

Travelling on the night of Sunday, July 13, from Washington, they arrived at Chicago on the Monday morning and boarded the express for Peoria where they were met by Dr. Coghill and Dr. G. E. Ward who entertained them to lunch before taking them in the afternoon to the Northern Regional Research Laboratory of the United States Department of Agriculture at Peoria. It was an immense new building of yellow brick, not yet completed, shaped like the letter U, with sides over a hundred yards long. Its many laboratories were situated on three floors and it was air-conditioned, with double windows, pressure-steam laid on to the laboratories from a central plant and all the most up-to-date equipment imaginable. Here they were introduced to Dr. O. E. May, the Director of the Laboratory, and they settled down to a general discussion of penicillin. The American scientists listened attentively. "Can you grow it in deep culture?" asked Dr. R. D. Coghill, who was Chief of the Fermentation Division in the Research Laboratory.

"I knew then that he was already starting to grapple with the problem," Florey once remarked.

As a result of that discussion, Dr. May and Dr. Coghill agreed to give the British scientists all the assistance possible and start work right away if they would show how the mould should be cultured and the penicillin extracted.

Consequently the next morning the two British scientists called at the laboratory to go more fully into the technical problems. They were received by Dr. Coghill and Dr. Ward who brought into the conference another member of the staff, Dr. A. J. Moyer, who was extremely reserved and who was deputed by Dr. Coghill to devote half his time to working with Dr. Heatley.

Let it be emphasized that Professor Florey and Dr. Heatley were scientists. They were not out to do business or to make money. After much travail, they and their colleagues in Oxford had achieved the seemingly impossible task of producing penicillin in a form in which it could be used to treat suffering humanity, and they aimed at one thing and one thing only—to save lives. They had no commercial designs or ambitions, they sought no personal profit. All they sought was more penicillin to carry out additional tests to find out the full scope of the new miracle drug so that it could be produced on a big enough scale to save those stricken down on the field of battle. They wanted to obtain penicillin quickly so that it could play its full part in the war. They had started their work in the days of peace. The results of their researches exceeded their expectations. Chain thought he would find an enzyme. They had found the chemotherapeutic substance of the medical world's dreams. Their utmost efforts could produce only small amounts and they wanted so much. They had no desire to see their work shelved until the war was over. Florey with all his drive and forthrightness was determined to do anything to prevent that, hence his mission to the United States.

"I became a carpet bagman trying to sell the idea of penicillin, but only two or three firms were interested in the United States and Canada," he admitted.

The brilliant work achieved by the Oxford team was not protected by patents in any way. Had they been so inclined, they might perhaps have protected the whole process by a series of patents. Heatley might have patented his method of extracting the penicillin from the ether with buffer; Chain might have taken out a patent for using amyl acetate; Abraham, Chain and Heatley between them might have covered the entire process with a series of patents that would have given them control over the production of penicillin throughout the world. But they did no such thing. Their sole desire was that mankind should enjoy the fruits of their work, which was indeed a glory to the British Commonwealth of Nations.

This was the incentive which prompted their visit to the United States; this was the feeling which animated them throughout. It must be stressed that wherever they went they gave the fullest details of all their processes. They answered all the questions to the best of their ability, they explained everything, they kept nothing back. They offered American scientists and chemical manufacturers the full and free use of their methods and processes and they asked nothing in return—except some penicillin to complete the clinical tests which would round off their researches.

Accordingly Dr. Heatley settled down in Peoria to help in culturing *Penicillium notatum*. The spell of hot weather which struck the British scientists in Lisbon and met them in New York persisted in Peoria. The temperature-controlled room in the new laboratory was not yet in operation and most of the time the temperature was above eighty-five degrees Fahrenheit. There was consequently some difficulty in inducing the mould to grow at all, for it disliked high temperatures and it had been subjected to them for so long that it was a wonder the cultures were not killed. But the scientists were experienced in the work, and by using all their skill they managed to get some cultures going, which made Heatley a little easier in his mind.

The main interest at first was to increase the low yield of penicillin by seeking a more suitable medium. Now yeast extract, as we know, had played an important part in speeding up the growth of the mould and it seemed to be a valuable ingredient of the medium. Experiments were therefore carried out with a dry preparation that did not give the desired results, so the suggestion was made to try corn-steep liquor.

Corn-steep liquor was something new to Heatley, but the American scientists were familiar with it, for it was one of the by-products of the local starch industry, and it had long been used in the yeast industry and as a growth promoter in other fermentations.

Fitting himself unobstrusively into American life, Heatley paid his dollar for a weekly ticket on the bus which took him to and from the laboratory morning and night. Step by step he demonstrated how they did things at Oxford, explaining in detail all the idiosyncrasies of the mould and any aspects of the work in which Moyer was interested. Heatley had drawn plans of the apparatus he had invented for the extraction of the penicillin and had written out full particulars which would enable any scientist to duplicate the process. These drawings and notes were so clear and concise that any intelligent man with a little scientific knowledge could follow them, and they were available if required.

The American scientist made his notes, asking questions freely concerning the medium and the behaviour of the mould, and Heatley drew upon his experience to answer as well as he could. When Heatley offered to show him how to do the assays, however, Dr. Moyer declined to undertake the task, consequently Heatley did the assays himself.

By 8.30 in the morning Heatley was at his bench starting his day's work. Sometimes his colleagues would take him down town by car at midday for lunch, and he would settle to work again about one o'clock and carry on until the laboratory staff eased off about six o'clock. If necessary he worked late at night, like the other research workers, and even on Sundays. He was glad to get on with his task. Everyone treated him with the greatest kindness and Dr. Coghill was always helpful.

The day after Heatley settled down to work in Peoria, Professor Florey hastened off to try to enlist the aid of American manufacturers. The British manufacturers could say with justification that they were fighting like the rest of the nation for their lives. That did not hold true of the Americans. They were making drugs for the British war effort. But they were not at war, struggling to get permits for raw materials, filling in endless forms to replace a worn-out bit of equipment, working the staff without rest and the plant without stopping for essential overhauls. Conditions in the United States were easier, which was why Professor Florey sought help there.

Everywhere he was received with the greatest courtesy. Here and there he found a chemist growing a flask or two of the mould. The Head of Mercks Research Department listened to all Florey told him and asked how he could help. "Will you brew and extract ten thousand litres and send the penicillin on to me for clinical trials?" he was asked.

H—m

OPPOSITE: *These giant towers at the national penicillin factory at Speke, near Liverpool, are gigantic air filters which trap the bacteria and sterilize all air in the sterile rooms and the great fermenters in which the mould grows to produce penicillin.*

The same question was put to the firm of Squibbs who showed a real desire to assist.

These were the most promising contacts made by Professor Florey. Everyone listened politely, although one manufacturer was very blunt. "I won't do anything without payment," he said.

Crossing the border into Canada, Florey went to visit a laboratory in Toronto. Then he went on to Montreal. Still full of determination, he made his way to Chicago, where Heatley joined him on August 23. They continued their pilgrimage, seeing this man and that, trying to provoke an interest in the precious drug that so few seemed to want. They saw more drug firms in New Jersey, and on September 4 Heatley called on Mercks to find they were indeed at work on penicillin. He told them and showed them as much as he could. He kept nothing back and found they were most receptive to new ideas. The keen interest in the work was accompanied by the greatest consideration, and at a later date he worked for six months in their laboratories, during which time they began to develop a method of growing the mould in trays fitted into large containers.

Separating from Professor Florey on September 13, Heatley returned to Peoria to continue the work there. When he got back he was delighted to find that the yield had been greatly increased by mixing a new medium, but Moyer did not tell Heatley what was the essential ingredient of the new formula. This did not worry Heatley, whose one desire was to see the work make progress. The more they cut down the period of growth and the higher they could raise the yield, the better it would be for mankind.

It was learned that, owing to the high temperature, much of the earlier work was disappointing; but a week later when the new temperature-controlled room came into operation for the first time, it was possible to make much better progress. Heatley was also able to teach a lady assistant, Mrs. Robertson, how to do the assays, and her skill and efficiency greatly eased his mind, for he was anxious not to leave Peoria without instructing someone how to do this important work.

In those days of 1941 the Fermentation Division was just starting under the direction of Dr. Coghill, whose assistants had been doing fermentation work in the U.S. Department of Agriculture and were therefore very experienced. At first and for some time all the moulds used at Peoria and in American factories were descendants of the mould which had planted itself on Fleming's plate and all the penicillin was derived from Fleming's mould. But the interest awakened by the work led to hundreds of strains of the mould being isolated from the soil in different parts of the world and these were methodically tested at Peoria and in other American laboratories in a wide effort to discover higher-yielding strains of *Penicillium notatum*.

As the magnitude of the work grew at Peoria, one scientist after another joined the staff to help to solve the many problems involved in the production of penicillin, until Dr. Coghill had gathered round him a team of scientists, as fine as the Oxford team, whose loyalty and selfless motives were beyond all question. They thought penicillin, talked penicillin and lived penicillin throughout their waking moments. Their enthusiasm was unbounded and the details of their brilliant accomplishments would fill a volume. Letters and telephone calls began to come to them from all over the United States. Manufacturers found their way to Peoria to learn all they could, chemists and research workers consulted them on a multitude of technicalities which kept them continually occupied. Peoria became the main focus point of all the penicillin knowledge in America. From one scientist who gave half his time to working with Heatley, the staff grew to twenty-five scientists and technical helpers who devoted all their time to the project.

New strains were cultured in hundreds by Dr. Kenneth B. Raper and his able assistant, Mrs. Dorothy Alexander, who spent their days prosecuting their search for more productive moulds. And before they could learn whether the new moulds were better or worse, it was necessary to test the medium on which they had been grown. This task kept Mr. W. H. Schmidt busy assaying the potency of the penicillin for ten hours a day and seven days a week. In their particular fields these workers were unexcelled and as a result of their intensive researches they were able to isolate moulds that yielded two hundred and three hundred per cent more penicillin than the strains that were cultured at Oxford. These new American strains eventually superseded all other moulds in commercial use in the United States and probably many strains in use in the United Kingdom, so it may be said with truth that up to the last days of 1945 the bulk of the penicillin produced in the world was derived from the new moulds isolated at Peoria.

While Dr. Coghill was away on missions connected with the work, Dr. G. E. Ward took charge and kept the organisation running, doing splendid work meantime in helping to develop the deep culture fermentation in tanks, which method was destined to become the most economic system of natural culture for commercial production.

Two other scientists in the team at Peoria, Dr. F. H. Stodola and Dr. J. L. Wachtel, not only perfected new methods for recovering greater quantities of penicillin from the brew, but they succeeded in isolating an entirely new penicillin which became known as Penicillin X or Penicillin III. They also did much secret work on the synthesis of the drug, while their colleague Dr. R. G. Benedict developed a new method for producing the enzyme known as penicillinase, a ferment most destructive to penicillin.

In this field Benedict was anticipated by Dr. E. F. Duthie of Oxford University who in 1944 published a method for making penicillinase that compares more than favourably with the American method. Penicillinase is the substance which is used to indicate whether penicillin is contaminated with unwanted bacteria, and it must be sufficiently potent to destroy the penicillin before the penicillin can destroy any contaminants. If the penicillinase were not very potent, it would take so long to destroy the penicillin that the miracle drug would have time to destroy the contaminating germs. The scientist making the test would therefore be entirely misled, because his result would show that the penicillin was not contaminated, whereas it was in fact contaminated when he started the test, although the penicillin managed to wipe out the germs before being wiped out itself by the penicillinase. Penicillinase produced by the Duthie method is so potent that one cubic centimetre of it will destroy one million units of penicillin in from twelve to eighteen hours. Usually the test is made with 100,000 units of penicillin which can be destroyed by two cubic centimetres of Duthie's penicillinase in an hour, or less, thus giving the penicillin no time to destroy any contaminating germs. It was Abraham and Chain who had the honour of discovering penicillinase in 1940, and up to the present no one has yet succeeded in isolating the substance in its pure state.

Directly the Peoria scientists learned that the new strains of mould selected by Raper and Alexander gave a much bigger yield on the corn-steep medium than had ever been obtained from the Fleming strains on the yeast medium, the fact was recognized as being of primary importance in the development of penicillin production. The incorporation of corn-steep liquor in the medium was in itself a remarkable stroke of luck for Peoria, which lay among the fertile prairies in what was called the corn-belt of the United States, with the Illinois River winding its way through it. The corn grown was maize, and not wheat which is generally called corn in Great Britain.

Now one of the main objects of the new government laboratory in Peoria was to find ways of utilizing some of the by-products of maize. Much of the maize of the corn-belt was turned into starch by the manufacturers who were blessed with exceptional natural conditions which provided an abundant water supply with a temperature that remained fairly constant summer and winter at about fifty-three degrees Fahrenheit. As previously mentioned, corn-steep liquor was one of the by-products of starch manufacture. Thus in one stroke the existence of the new laboratory was justified by the discovery of a valuable use for a by-product of maize which aided to a considerable degree the economic development of penicillin. In this way the Gods of Chance operated once more to the advantage of mankind.

Nothing can belittle the fine work done at Peoria nor the humanitarian motives of those who strove so hard to enable sufficient penicillin to be produced in time to aid the war effort.

It is of passing interest that in due course Dr. A. J. Moyer applied for certain patents in the United States. And on May 31, 1945, his agents lodged three patent applications in the Patent Office, London, where they were stamped with the numbers 13674, 13675 and 13676. His first English application was for culturing *Penicillium notatum* in eight different ways, including deep culture in which the mould was grown submerged in the medium and also in a state of agitation while oxygen or a gas containing oxygen was passed through the medium—Dr. Reid's earlier experiments with oxygen will be remembered. His second application claimed patents for thirty-nine different media, many in combination with corn-steep liquor; and the third application was for adding periodically or continuously to the medium some assimilable carbon to enable the mould to continue the process of creating penicillin—he also claimed for withdrawing some of the medium after the mould had grown for one or two days and replacing a similar quantity of medium—as Heatley used to do in the early days at Oxford. In these three English applications he claimed patents for growing the mould on the surface of various corn-steep and other media, growing it submerged in tanks, growing it in rotating drums and growing it in large bottles in a state of agitation while air was being passed through the medium.

Concerning these and other applications for patents, there is on record the opinion of Dr. Charles Thom, the famous American mycologist and an official of the United States Department of Agriculture, who stated in *Mycologia* for July-August, 1945: "It is equally doubtful to the discriminating spectator who has watched the development of practices and listened to the claims, whether any of the 'patents applied for' honestly represent valid claims to originality."

A later search at the Patent Office in London disclosed that two other American scientists, J. W. Foster and L. E. McDaniel, applied for patents for growing penicillin in deep culture on corn-steep liquor on May 15, 1944, thus anticipating by sixteen days Dr. Moyer's applications and adding a further complication to the position.

At a dinner given in his honour in New York in June, 1945, Sir Alexander Fleming mentioned the applications for patents in connection with penicillin: "When the basic information was given free to the world, it seems a pity that people here and there should seek to make capital out of what is, after all, a matter of detail," he said to the distinguished gathering.

Seeking enlightenment from the American Embassy in London, I learned that an official of the United States Department of Agriculture "is able to take out a patent, but the patent becomes the property of the United States Government." Such patents by officials of the Northern Regional Research Laboratory at Peoria would be assigned to the Secretary of Agriculture, so if Dr. Moyer's applications for patents were granted in the United States—they had not been granted up to the beginning of April, 1946—the American people would still enjoy their free use without having to pay any royalties on penicillin.

According to the rules of the United States Department of Agriculture, its scientists retain all foreign rights in their inventions and discoveries, so Dr. Moyer did what he was legally entitled to do in applying for patents in the United Kingdom. Consequently if these patents were granted, the British people would be obliged to pay royalties to Foster and McDaniel or Dr. Moyer on every dose of penicillin made in Great Britain on corn-steep medium and in deep culture, while the American people, on the other hand, would continue to enjoy the free use of all the technical knowledge concerning the great basic discovery of penicillin which the British scientists gave freely without hesitation to Dr. Moyer and the American nation.

To revert to the days of September, 1941, Professor Florey's last gesture to aid production before leaving the United States was to call on Dr. A. N. Richards, under whom he had worked in the laboratories in Pennsylvania for some months in 1925. Dr. Richards had but recently been appointed the Chairman of the Committee of Medical Research in the Office of Scientific Research and Development. He greeted Professor Florey warmly and, after the usual preliminaries, asked: "Well, what can I do for you?"

Florey told him as concisely as possible about penicillin and urged him to try to induce the American Government to produce the drug.

Dr. Richards promised to do what he could. And Florey, as he shook him by the hand, knew that he would keep his word. He did, and in the United States it is generally acknowledged that Dr. A. N. Richards was largely responsible for getting penicillin produced on a big scale, consequently the personal contact which Florey had made in earlier years proved of supreme importance in providing the world with penicillin.

As Florey left the United States to return to England, he reviewed his efforts of the last few months. He had induced Dr. Coghill of Peoria to start producing penicillin and the work was making good progress; two chemical manufacturers had promised to brew and extract ten thousand litres and send the penicillin to Oxford for further clinical trials; and Dr. A. N. Richards had approved the work and promised to do what he could.

If it was not as much as Professor Florey hoped, at any rate he could claim with truth that he had started the United States on the road to producing the precious drug.

CHAPTER XI

THE STRUGGLE FOR PRODUCTION

DURING the absence in America of Professor Florey and Dr. Heatley, the work of producing penicillin in Oxford fell upon Dr. Chain, who was anxious to evolve methods to speed up production and eliminate the risk of the penicillin being destroyed by air-borne bacteria. Had there been air-conditioning plant installed in the laboratories, his task would have been simplified, for he could have filtered out the atmospheric dust and germs and obviated much of the risk. Lacking such an installation, he sought to attain his end by different means. Dust was the enemy of penicillin. However daintily the Penicillin Girls moved about the laboratory, every step they took on the floor displaced a certain amount of air and created a tiny current which, imperceptible as it was, could carry the bacteria that destroyed the penicillin. To ensure that no speck of dust remained on the floors or lodged on the intricate apparatus dotted about the benches in the laboratory was almost an impossibility. No vacuum cleaner could have done what Dr. Chain desired, although he used one borrowed from his home.

For the rest, he had the floor covered with spindle oil to trap any bacteria or speck of dust that happened to drop down on it from the air. The benches at which the girls worked were flooded with paraffin oil to serve the same purpose—that no speck of dust should be free to float about the room and any germs which alighted on floor or bench would be held fast at once. The theory was sound. But the liberal use of oil led to many a burst of laughter as a girl felt the legs of the stool glide from under her on the slippery floor. They worked very happily together, and if one sat unexpectedly on the floor, or another, washing out the culture vessels, happened in her haste to let the upright jet of water swamp her hair and face, it was something to laugh over.

The girls themselves were dressed in sterile white overalls, a mob cap to cover their hair, a mask over their faces, rubber gloves for their hands, and goloshes for their feet, all of which were sterilized. In this way Dr. Chain sought to avoid contamination from their clothes.

Once a month the girls went off to the bureau with a trolley to collect the yeast for the medium. They boiled it in white enamel buckets before pouring it into four-litre flasks with which they loaded the trolley to convey them to the centrifuge. The yeast not wanted for immediate requirements was stored in the ice chest with chloroform to keep it. And the trolley with its load of bottles was, as one pretty girl put it, "wheeled upstairs in the lift."

To expedite the filling of the culture vessels, Dr. Chain installed a big tank in the roof which was filled with the medium. This was carried by its own gravity down glass pipes to the culture room where it passed through a Seitz filter into large ten-litre sterilized bottles from which it was blown by compressed air into the culture vessels.

Over the door of the room hung a heavy curtain to exclude dust. This was cleaned regularly with the vacuum cleaner. And outside the door was a large white enamel pan marked BREAD which was filled with hot lysol, into which the girls used to dip the bottles of medium up to the necks to sterilize the outsides before pushing aside the curtain and handing them to one of the girls inside. Before a girl was allowed to go inside the incubating room, she had to stand in her rubber goloshes in a tray full of lysol to ensure that she carried no bacteria upon her footwear.

Despite these precautions, Dr. Chain found that contamination still took place and he was sometimes under the necessity of scrapping whole batches of culture. This waste of material and time delayed the experiments which Dr. Chain and Dr. Abraham were making on the purification process. Nevertheless they made progress and slowly collected a little stock of penicillin against the day when it would be required for further clinical tests.

In late October Professor Florey returned to Oxford from his mission in the United States. The position seemed brighter, for he was fortified by definite promises to send on the penicillin yielded by ten thousand litres of brew. Added to what they could produce in Oxford, this would provide enough for a clinical test on a wider scale than before. Accordingly Professor Florey went ahead with his plans, thinking that a fair supply of penicillin was assured for the patients and that he would not again have to endure the painful sight of watching a patient who was well on the road to recovery suffer a sudden relapse owing to the exhaustion of the precious drug. That was something which he was bent on avoiding in future.

While plans were being made for these tests, Chain and Abraham were engrossed in the chemical problems of purification and concentration; the Penicillin Girls, wrapped up to the ears, rolled the great bottles up and down their knees in the cold room; while Dr. A. G. Sanders exercised his ingenuity in creating a new type of extraction plant in a building at the end of the grounds.

It was a large, lofty room, about eleven feet high, with walls and woodwork painted a primrose yellow. Built as a mortuary, it had two great doors at the side. "They could have done a post-mortem on an elephant here," Heatley remarked with truth. Just inside the normal entrance door was a six-foot porcelain bath with hot and cold water. Two windows on the wall opposite the door gave the place ample light, while there was a sink with a slate bench by one of the windows and a basin with running water along the wall to the left.

Here Dr. Sanders worked methodically like a mechanic for month after month, measuring timber and cutting it up for racks and shelves and stagings and then, assisted by Mr. Kent, screwing the racks together and fixing them in place. The scientist was an orderly man. He believed in having a place for everything and seeing that everything was in its place, and on the shelves in the laboratory were neat stacks of little boxes marked with the names of their contents, such as "Fibre Washers", or "Large Nuts", "Dowel Screws", "Hypo Needles", "Gas Jets", and so on through the whole gamut of things useful in building special apparatus.

Juggling with great lengths of three-quarter inch pipe, he cut them and turned threads upon them to join them up with various bends to go in different directions to serve diverse purposes. The scientist, displaying the efficiency of a trained plumber, proved that an intelligent man can use his hands as well as his brain. Gradually a conglomeration of green and brown and red metal pipes, interspersed with lengths of glass pipes and red rubber tubing, began to gather about eight ordinary ten-gallon milk churns, each of which Dr. Sanders drilled underneath to take an outflow pipe and stopcock. To control the process at all stages, Dr. Sanders inserted stopcocks in the pipes to check the inflow or outflow wherever necessary. He left nothing to chance. High above everything, just under the electric fan in the ceiling which was installed to ventilate the room and suck out any fumes, were two big tanks placed side by side, with another tank perched between them on top. These contained the large supplies of amyl acetate used in the extraction. An ordinary milk-cooler such as the farmer uses to reduce the temperature of milk was installed on the right-hand wall and connected by pipes with the outflow of the porcelain bath; while electric pumps were slipped into the circuit here and there to force the fluid on to the next stage of the process.

As correct extraction depended upon combining the exact proportions of different fluids, Dr. Sanders did everything he could think of to eliminate the possibility of errors arising during a moment's distraction on another task. Glass gauges outside the churns gave the exact level of the fluid inside. To the set of churns placed on the opposite side of the staging he fitted little drums marked with the words EMPTY, FILLING, SECOND EXTRACTION, etc., which could be turned with a flick of the finger to indicate the stage that the process had reached, so that a girl could attend to something else and make no mistake in recalling the exact stage of the process. Between the two banks of churns two centrifuges were set up on solid concrete beds to eliminate the vibration, though nothing could lessen the whine they made when they were turning at 15,000 revolutions a minute.

When the mould was ready to harvest, the brew was poured from the culture vessels into milk churns on trolleys, the mould was pressed to extract the last drop of penicillin fluid from it, and the churns were wheeled to the extraction house by two of the Penicillin Girls or two male assistants who tipped the brew into the bath just inside the door. From the bath it was pumped up to the top of the cooler over which it streamed from a multitude of tiny jets to be caught in the gutter at the bottom of the cooler and conducted by a pipe overhead to a churn on the other side of the gangway.

Directly the exact quantity of amyl acetate had flowed into a churn, the chilled penicillin fluid followed and a sample was taken to test its alkalinity by placing a drop in a little china dish divided into a dozen little depressions, not unlike the little dishes used by children to mix their water colours; a drop of the stain was added, and the girl knew instantly by the change in colour how alkaline was the crude penicillin. Then she turned the tap to let the sulphuric acid flow in to acidify the crude medium, testing this again in the same way by adding a spot of stain. And when the mixture was sufficiently acid, she took a metal plunger or paddle, containing a series of holes and gave a few strokes up and down to mix the fluids thoroughly, before running the mixture quickly into the centrifuge.

Spinning at a dizzy speed, the centrifuge separated the heavier water and protein from the amyl acetate in which the penicillin was dissolved and the waste medium ran away down a drain while the amyl acetate containing the penicillin flowed to the left into another churn where a certain quantity of water was mixed with it and also a carefully-measured amount of bicarbonate solution to draw the penicillin out of the amyl acetate into the water. The liquids were mixed and allowed to stand, whereupon the water containing the penicillin settled at the bottom of the churn, from which it was drawn off by air suction into a bottle in which further separation could be watched by the operator. When the correct degree of separation was attained, the girl turned another stop-cock to let the amber penicillin fluid run into another bottle, watching carefully to exclude any amyl acetate, then she ran the amyl acetate back into the churn for another washing, otherwise to be mixed with water again to extract any penicillin that remained in it. After three or four further treatments the penicillin fluid was handed over to Dr. Chain and Dr. Abraham for purification.

From time to time the centrifuge had to be dismantled and stripped of the jelly-like mass formed by the proteins of the mould and medium and it was a heartening sight to see a pretty girl handling the heavy cylinder, cleaning it out expertly with a metal scraper, washing it under running water and setting it up and locking it home like an experienced engineer.

Meanwhile Professor Florey waited expectantly for the penicillin from the United States. The New Year dawned, but no penicillin arrived. The weeks slipped by. Still there was nothing from America.

"We must increase production here," he said and the whole team toiled to brew 500 litres a week. Another effort was made to interest some of the British chemical manufacturers and this time the chief chemist of Kemball, Bishop and Company went to Oxford to see Professor Florey.

"I saw the process and had a long discussion with Professor Florey. He was very enthusiastic about some of the results he had obtained and was anxious to secure more penicillin to test it. His enthusiasm touched me and his cures decided us to do what we could to help. I told him we would try to grow the stuff and do our best to assist him," the chief chemist remarked to me.

So he returned to the East End of London where the chemical works stood amid a desolation of destruction. The surrounding ruins disclosed with dramatic emphasis why the chemical manufacturers of Great Britain found it difficult to embark on anything new. By some miracle the works were spared when adjoining buildings and whole streets were going up in flames during the

Luftwaffe's fierce attempt to wipe out London. More than once
their escapes were providential. A member of the night shift entered
the works one night during the black-out cursing because he had
just stumbled over something in the road. The chief engineer,
wondering what the obstruction was, went out to see. By the light
of his torch he found a five hundred pound German bomb embedded
in the road outside the office window with the detonator pointing
upward. How the man failed to touch it off and blow himself and
the works to pieces when he fell over it still remains a mystery.
Another night the place was plastered with incendiary bombs.
Several fell upon the roof of the factory, where the chief engineer
was dealing with three while a workman was tackling two others.

"There's another fire," said the chief engineer, seeing one start
up a short distance away.

"Yes, and it's your 'ouse," said the workman.

And it was.

On another occasion their look-out watched a German bomber
flying straight towards the works, dropping his bombs at regular
intervals. The spotter, marking the fall of each bomb, gave the
signal for the workers to take cover. It seemed that nothing could
save the works, that the next bomb would fall right on them, when
in the most freakish manner the pilot changed course and the works
were spared.

There was the never-to-be-forgotten night when the distillery
on the other side of the River Lee was hit by a German bomber and
thousands of gallons of burning spirit flowed over the Lee and
turned it into a river of fire. When the managing director arrived
at the chemical works next morning he found thirteen hogsheads of
spirit lying in the yard.

"What's this?" he asked.

"It's spirit the men have fished out of the river," was the reply.

That chemical works was very precious to the managing director
and still more precious to the nation. He visualised what would
happen if they got another burst of incendiaries that night. "Get
into touch with the owners and cart these hogsheads out of the
yard at once. They mustn't remain on the premises," was the stern
order.

The offices of the firm were decidedly mid-Victorian, but the
management was so up-to-date and far-sighted that the pact of
Munich, which lulled so many people into a sense of false security,
set them training their staff in first-aid, fire-fighting, and in observing

aircraft until by June, 1939, the staff was organized for anything that might happen. The consequence was that while the staffs in Government offices and factories were taking cover during the early raids, the people here worked on and did not take cover until their spotters on the roof gave them warning. They were all very keen to look after the interests of the firm, as I personally discovered, and there was never any staff trouble from the beginning to the end of the war.

As soon as the chief chemist got back from Oxford he conferred with his managing director before calling together the technical staff to let them worry over the problems of penicillin. They concluded that it was impossible to have large-scale production by manufacturing in bottles. At Oxford they visualized the bottle as the unit, but here they visualized the room as the unit which would enable them to expand production to any extent, so they decided to try the open-tray production.

This was the first revolutionary idea in the production of penicillin. It seemed to be courting failure, for when sterilized vessels plugged with sterile cotton wool became contaminated, how was it possible to prevent the air-borne bacteria from contaminating the open trays? Nevertheless this method was decided upon and this was the plan which they were determined to carry through to success. They were quite familiar with fermentation—they had been manufacturing chemicals by a fermentation process for years—and they consequently had a good idea of some of the difficulties that faced them. Calling in an expert to test samples of the air in the factory, they soon learned that the atmosphere was extremely rich in bacteria and so full of impurities that it was quite unfitted for penicillin production. That was not helpful.

"We must show you our Heath Robinson plant," the managing director said, and took me through to the ground floor of the research laboratory where they made their initial experiments to produce penicillin by the open-tray method. They started with the advantage of two rooms that had already been fitted for fermentation. An air-conditioning plant purified the air and heated it to the right temperature before allowing it to flow along an eight-inch trunkway to the incubating rooms. These resembled two cells about nine feet long, four feet wide and eight feet high. Along one side of each room were metal racks to take four tiers of aluminium trays which were about two feet long, a foot wide and two inches deep. Each contained a hundred trays, with air-tight doors and thermostats to control the temperature; there was a big drain in the floor to allow of flushing, and an inflowing air duct low down by the door with an air outflow high on the wall at the other end of the cell. The rooms were completely enclosed, without windows, and one was finished in white tiles, while the walls of the other were rough cement covered with aluminium paint. The mysterious thing was that the room painted with aluminium always gave a greater yield than the other, although the only difference that I could see was the way in which the walls were finished.

"We never could understand why it was," the chief chemist remarked. I personally suspect the aluminium paint.

Although they were so well versed in the process of fermentation, they had to confess that brewing penicillin presented them with some entirely new problems of extraordinary difficulty. Experiment followed experiment. They were haunted by the bugbear of contamination. They spent their money as freely as their time in their efforts to help Professor Florey. This London chemical works contained a team of technical workers as keen and united as the team of scientists at Oxford. They were determined to succeed. And in the end they perfected their process of brewing penicillin by the open-tray method.

It was a great day when the managing director was able to write to Professor Florey to advise him that the first brew was ready, and on September 11, 1942, twenty churns were loaded on the lorry in Kemball, Bishop's yard at Bromley-by-Bow and conveyed to Oxford. Its arrival gladdened the hearts of all the workers at Oxford, particularly Professor Florey, to whom this two hundred gallons of penicillin brew opened up the prospect of carrying out more clinical trials.

Thenceforward a lorry full of churns containing the penicillin brew was driven from Bromley-by-Bow to Oxford every week, and Kemball, Bishop and Company achieved the honour of being the first commercial firm to brew penicillin by a new method on a scale which could be expanded to any degree. There were some weeks when the lorry did not draw up before the School of Pathology, unfortunate weeks when the devilish bacteria had managed to creep into the incubating rooms and spoil the whole brew. There was nothing to be done about it except to pour the whole lot down the drain and start a fresh lot of cultures.

"They kept their promise," said Professor Florey to me in mentioning the help they gave, and in these days when promises are easily made and broken without compunction, that is a high tribute. In keeping their promise they made a niche for themselves in medical history. Their skill in brewing penicillin in a new way was matched by their generosity, for they paid all the expenses and sent up a weekly supply of brew to Oxford for over a year.

"It was a free gift in the interest of science," I was told.

Before I left this factory which had miraculously survived the destruction of the German bombing raids, I was privileged to glance at the latest culture rooms where the mould was grown. All had recently been cleared and the staff were sterilizing them and restocking them after a holiday. It happened that Victory Day in Europe came when the cultures were only half grown and a staff holiday would have interfered with the biological process and wasted the whole brew. The matter was placed before them frankly by the foreman, and their loyalty and sense of duty was proved when every member of the staff voted for continuing the process until it was finished and taking their holiday afterwards. That was true co-operation.

A white-coated young scientist switched on a light inside one of the rooms and I peered through the little observation glass to the long lines of aluminium trays half full of a chocolate-coloured fluid with streaks of white appearing on it as though someone had begun to stir in cream and had left the task unfinished. Those white streaks were the spores of the mould starting to make good growth.

"When did you start it up," asked the chief chemist.

"Yesterday," was the reply.

"It seems to be doing very well," I remarked, and went to peep through the observation window of another room. It was full of a steamy white fog and through the crack of the door seeped something which made my eyes smart. They were sterilizing the room with formaldehyde to destroy all the bacteria before stocking it with new cultures. How they managed to introduce the trays full of medium into the room without admitting more bacteria was their secret. It must be done, but they were discreetly silent about how it was accomplished. On a little black square upon the doors were chalked the figures 78-80 to indicate the temperature of the room inside. All the original rooms were constructed to take a hundred trays of culture, but the latest room was doubled in size to take two hundred trays. As an indication of the handicap imposed by the war, I may mention that apparatus ordered over two years earlier had not been delivered when I visited the works to learn how they had aided Professor Florey.

OPPOSITE: *Using spray-guns in the Burroughs, Wellcome laboratory at Beckenham to inoculate bottles of medium with spores of the mould which produces penicillin. Air pressure was kept high in the chamber so that the air flowed outwards and carried bacteria away. This fine new factory was closed in June 1946 because it could not compete with the latest deep-culture plants.*

The penicillin extracted from this generous gift of Kemball, Bishop served mankind well in the clinical experiments which it helped Professor Florey to carry out. Eventually he received from the firm of Mercks in the United States a small supply, amounting to 500,000 units. Yet it was a most welcome addition to the meagre stock that was being gathered with such patience in the refrigerator of the Sir William Dunn School of Pathology and no less welcome was the penicillin sent by the Imperial Chemical Industries.

OPPOSITE: *Above is the big cylindrical incubator which was used by the Imperial Chemical Industries to develop their open-tray method of culturing the mould to produce penicillin. Below is the air-conditioning plant in the laboratories of Boots.*

CHAPTER XII

BACK FROM THE GRAVE

BADLY as Professor Florey wanted every grain of penicillin for further clinical trials, he was far-sighted enough to subordinate his immediate object to his main aim, which was to help the men wounded in the war. The gallantry of the Royal Air Force in those days stirred and sustained the whole nation and in June, 1942, Professor Florey denuded his small supply of penicillin that had been garnered with so much labour by the Oxford scientists and handed over a moiety to Flight Lieutenant D. C. Bodenham to see if it would help to heal the courageous young airmen who were burned in battle.

Bodenham was dealing with burns and these first few grammes of penicillin, which contained no more than seven units per milligramme, initiated a series of tests extending over the next eighteen months and embracing over seventy cases of burns on all parts of the body from head to foot. During this time Chain and Abraham made such strides in the purification that the penicillin received by Bodenham went up to one hundred and sixty units per milligramme. Bodenham at first tried dusting the powdered calcium salt of penicillin on the burned surfaces. It was wasteful, so he mixed a little penicillin with a large quantity of sulphanilamide powder and found it more effective. This powder was also very helpful in skin-grafting which was so largely employed in the treatment of burns. But his most successful treatment was achieved with a penicillin cream made from lanette wax, vaseline and water to which he added a solution of penicillin.

Having set in train these experiments in the Royal Air Force in June, the Oxford team made a small quantity of penicillin to send some out in July to Lieutenant-Colonel R. J. V. Pulvertaft in Cairo for use on a few wounded in the desert campaigns. These tests were so successful that efforts were made to produce penicillin in Cairo. Thus by the middle of 1942 the scientists began to reach out toward their main goal—to save the wounded.

What they were most anxious to do now was to find out the best way of administering the drug, to learn the minimum dose that would be effective and discover how often it should be given. These were the main factors of treatment, although many more subsidiary items had a bearing on it. The easiest way of administering medicine is by mouth—"The Mixture to be taken three times a day in a little water after meals". But they were aware that the gastric juices were inimical to penicillin. They were equally aware that if some method could be found of overcoming this drawback, treatment by mouth was the ideal way.

Accordingly a dose of penicillin was made up into a capsule with a coating of material impervious to the acids of the stomach and a healthy man took it just before breakfast. At the end of an hour a blood sample showed a trace of penicillin, at the end of two hours there was enough penicillin in the blood to stop the test germ from growing, but by the end of three hours all detectable trace of penicillin had vanished from the blood, although penicillin was filtering out through the kidneys for another four hours. A second capsule with double the dose of penicillin was coated with a skin so acid-proof that the penicillin could not escape until nearly six hours after it was taken.

This was not very promising. Nevertheless it was decided to treat two cases by mouth. Each patient was given 480,000 units of penicillin without much effect, whereupon the method was discontinued, after depleting the stock of penicillin by nearly a million units.

It may generally be accepted that the bigger the body to be treated by injections, the bigger the quantity needed to effect a cure. A short, thin woman would need less than a tall, fat man, a half-grown girl less than a big woman and a baby least of all because it was so very small. So a little baby only two months old and weighing no more than seven and a half pounds was given penicillin by Dr. Ethel Florey in an effort to cure it of osteomyelitis, a dread disease of the bones, caused by the *Staphylococcus aureus* which was susceptible to penicillin. Many injections were made into a muscle, varied by several injections into a vein, with other injections into the abcesses from which the baby suffered. In this case penicillin proved to be a boon indeed, for a total of 100,800 units saved the baby in twenty days. Seven months later, he had more than doubled in weight and bore no trace of his early deformities. The physicians, using the X-Rays, peeped at the bones in his body and saw by the shadows they cast that they were building up very well, while the boy himself was healthy and active.

So as suitable cases presented themselves—and suitable cases generally meant cases that could make no headway with other known treatments—the precious stock of penicillin was drawn upon and some new fact was noted about the treatment. It was learned that doses of 40,000 units could be injected into a vein without harming the patient and that the treatment could be carried on for weeks without causing any toxic symptoms. Time and again the harmlessness of penicillin was proved, time and again its curative effects against sensitive bacteria were seen.

Eleven cases had been treated and studied when the telephone rang on August 6, 1942, and Professor Florey picked it up to answer a London call. He heard the voice of Professor Fleming speak to him from St. Mary's Hospital to describe the case of a dying friend for whom penicillin was a last hope. The patient who was moribund suffered from streptococcal meningitis, and Fleming had proved for himself that the streptococcus infecting the patient was very vulnerable to the drug.

"If you could spare some penicillin, I would like to try it," Fleming said.

"We have so little," Florey explained. "But I will gladly do all I can providing you allow us to include your case in our records."

That decision proclaimed Florey's scientific integrity. It showed that he was not interested in selecting easy cases to build up the reputation of penicillin, but that his sole interest was to see exactly what penicillin could do even in the most adverse case. "Would you permit us to include your case in our records?" he asked.

"Certainly," agreed Fleming.

"All right. I will bring some down to you," said Florey, who caught the next train to London and walked straight out of Paddington Station into St. Mary's Hospital a few yards away, where he met Professor Fleming, and showed him the magic yellow powder. On that day of August 6, 1942, Fleming looked upon concentrated penicillin for the first time. He had never seen it before. Fourteen years earlier he felt sure that something like it must exist, his experiments clearly proved it, but although he had tried so desperately to find it he had been obliged at last to relinquish the search. So the scientist who had dreamed of penicillin and the scientist who had made the dream come true discussed the dying man in the ward of St. Mary's Hospital. Giving Fleming full instructions how to use the penicillin and saying that he would bring more along in a day or two when it was ready, Florey went back to Oxford and left Professor Alexander Fleming to fight for his friend's life.

The patient was an oculist, aged fifty-two, who was taken ill on

June 18 and started to run a temperature. Though not a high fever, it persisted until the end of June and his doctor could not find out the cause. Failing to improve, the patient was taken to St. Mary's Hospital on July 7, still suffering from fever, with a temperature of 100.2 F. His condition completely baffled the physicians who were unable to diagnose the disease which afflicted him.

For a week he puzzled the doctors who had him under observation, then his stiff neck and drowsy condition suggested meningitis. They drew some fluid from his spine in the hope of finding the infective organism, but found only harmless germs. At the same time they gave him sulphapyradine which succeeded in bringing his temperature down to normal without improving his mental condition, for he continued to ramble in his speech and remained very drowsy. Four days later they withdrew more spinal fluid to try to find the germ. Again they could find nothing to account for the patient's condition. After a week's treatment, the sulphapyradine was stopped and next day his temperature rose again. He was very sick, his mind very confused.

On July 24 a little more spinal fluid was withdrawn, yet no coccus could be found to account for the meningitis. It was unusual. The patient began to lose control of his bodily functions. Worst of all he began to hiccough and nothing the physicians could do would stop it. They varied his treatment by putting him on to another sulpha compound, sulphathiazole, but it made no difference to his condition.

Distressed at the state of his friend, Fleming, like the other physicians, was mystified at being unable to find the infective organism. On August 1 they made another attempt. This time instead of trying to culture the organisms on solid agar medium, they tried it on a very soft "sloppy" mixture of glucose and agar. They were at a loss no longer. The germ was found. They observed twenty colonies of a streptococcus.

Three days later they drew a little more spinal fluid to culture the cocci on five different media to study their growth before Fleming tested them against sulphathiazole and some penicillin broth which he had prepared. The sulphathiazole was harmless to the coccus, but the penicillin wiped out the germ within a radius of eleven millimetres. Still uncertain that it was this germ which was killing the patient before their eyes, the physicians resolved their doubts. Mixing the germs with a little of the patient's blood, they found the cocci quickly collected into clumps, which proved that the defences in the patient's blood were fighting this particular germ; but in

testing a dozen normal sera from healthy people the cocci remained
dispersed and showed no inclination to clump. Fleming needed no
further evidence. On the night of August 5 the patient was in such a
bad state that it was necessary to inject a heart stimulant and administer oxygen. The next morning Professor Fleming rang up
Professor Florey, as we know, to ask for some penicillin to save his
friend.

This is what Professor Fleming wrote of the patient when the
injections of penicillin were started on the evening of August 6.
"The patient was in a very bad state and appeared to be dying. He
took little food; had been for days drowsy with occasional bouts of
extreme restlessness; now drowsy, comatose, wandering and ram-
bling; had been suffering from uncontrollable hiccough for ten
days. . . . On the evening of August 6, two-hourly intramuscular
injections of penicillin were begun. In twenty-four hours the patient
was mentally clearer, his hiccough had disappeared and head-re-
traction was less marked. Temperature had fallen to ninety-seven
degrees F."

After giving the patient sixty injections in five days, Professor
Fleming decided to inject the penicillin direct into the spinal column
so that it could diffuse through the cerebrospinal fluid and attack
the germs which were affecting the brain. This had never been done
before with penicillin and was a new departure. An injection of 5,000
units of penicillin was given. Meanwhile the injections into the
muscle every two hours were continued.

Several other injections were made direct into the spine, and as the
patient complained of tiredness owing to lack of sleep, which was not
surprising considering that he was disturbed every two hours to have
an injection, the injections during the night were stopped. The last
injection of 5,000 units into the fluid of the spine was made on August
19.

By August 28 he got up for the first time. His temperature had
been normal for a fortnight and there was no sign of meningitis. On
September 9, according to his case record, he "left hospital
apparently well." Let me quote again. "September 24, 1943 (thirteen
months afterwards). Patient has remained well. Recovery complete."
And in 1946 he was still well.

To Professor Fleming it was a miracle. The 1,627,500 units of
penicillin so generously provided by Professor Florey had rescued
the patient from the grave.

Hopeful as Professor Fleming had always been about penicillin, this demonstration of the curative powers of the impure drug exceeded anything he had imagined. This was no drug to be turned out on a small scale, but something so vital to humanity that it ought to be made in a big way. Thinking it over, he concluded that the whole force of the British Government should be concentrated on making it. But the British Government already had its hands more than full in making weapons of war. How was it possible to induce them to start making penicillin at this juncture? He did not know, so he went along to discuss the matter with Professor Raistrick, to whom he described the miracle recently worked by penicillin at St. Mary's Hospital.

"What is the best way of getting the Government to take it up?" he asked Raistrick.

"The best way would be to go straight to the Prime Minister," said Raistrick. "Do you know Mr. Churchill?"

"No," replied Fleming. "But I know the Minister of Supply."

"I'd go to him straight away," urged Raistrick.

Fleming lost no time. He rang up his friend Sir Andrew Duncan, the Minister of Supply, and arranged a meeting at which he told the Minister how a dying man was saved by penicillin, without which all the known drugs and the greatest medical skill in the world would have been useless. Thus as a direct result of the consultation between Fleming and Raistrick, the British Government became interested in the manufacture of penicillin.

Inquiries soon revealed to the Minister of Supply that if penicillin was the most difficult stuff in the world to produce, it was well worth going to any trouble and expense to obtain it. He discussed the matter with Sir Cecil Weir, the Director-General of Equipment and Stores in whose department was the Directorate of Medical Supplies.

"We've just been considering whether something could now be done to get factory production going," said Sir Cecil Weir.

"Let us get on with it quickly. Everything possible must be done to get this stuff for the troops," rejoined the Minister of Supply.

Accordingly a meeting was called on September 25, 1942, of all who were working to produce penicillin or who could give any help in its production. Fleming's friend who had made such a marvellous recovery was not discharged from St. Mary's Hospital until September 9 and within the short space of sixteen days most of the experts on penicillin in the country were gathered round the great table in Sir Cecil Weir's room, through the window of which one of Epstein's monstrous statues could be seen close by.

When Sir Cecil Weir took the chair, there were present Mr. Arthur Mortimer, Lieutenant-Colonel Sir Russell Wilkinson and other officials of the Ministry of Supply; Major-General L. T. Poole and Lieutenant-Colonel H. J. Bensted of the Pathological Department of the Army Medical Directorate; Professor Alexander Fleming, Professor Howard Florey and Professor Harold Raistrick who between them knew more about penicillin than anyone in the world; Dr. C. J. T. Cronshaw, Dr. C. M. Scott and Mr. A. J. Quig represented the Imperial Chemical Industries; Dr. T. B. Maxwell, Dr. F. H. Carr, Dr. F. W. Pyman and Dr. J. Trevan came from the Therapeutic Research Corporation; and Mr. E. A. Quill and Mr. W. A. R. Wilks represented Kemball, Bishop and Company.

"The Minister of Supply is very much interested in the potentialities of penicillin," said Sir Cecil Weir. "That is the reason why I have asked you to come here. He has given instructions that the Directorate of Medical Supplies should do everything possible to ensure that all the available knowledge of the drug is pooled so that research can be concentrated upon producing penicillin on a factory scale. Nothing need stand in the way. The Government is prepared to give financial assistance wherever it is required. We want all the producers, the potential producers and those engaged on experimental work to get together and share their knowledge and experience in order to produce the drug quickly."

To ask chemical firms in commercial competition with each other to share their secrets was making a big demand on them, and while they were all willing to work together for the public good, some were restrained by contracts with associated firms from making such disclosures offhand. However, these members stated that they would be glad to pool their knowledge if they were permitted to do so by their associates whose consent, they believed, would be freely given.

Professor Florey told the meeting how he had given American firms free access to all available information at the disposal of the School of Pathology in Oxford University, as he had also done to British firms. He thought there should be complete reciprocity with a full interchange of information now that production was developing, and he was uneasy about the tendency of certain people to take out patents. The Therapeutic Research Corporation's representatives made it clear that information supplied to them from America would be shared with Professor Florey, Professor Raistrick and other scientific workers in Great Britain.

Thereafter the discussion opened out into all the problems of production, the provision of raw materials, of plant and buildings, with the amounts of penicillin required for different types of case, the amounts of brew already being produced and the quantities likely to be required in the future. Everything that was likely to expedite the production of penicillin was discussed and by the time the meeting ended all those present who possessed the necessary freedom of action had agreed to pool their information and work continuously together for the common end. Incidentally, those who had been obliged to make reservations were permitted by their associate firms to contribute all the knowledge they possessed.

"I would like to thank you, gentlemen, for the co-operative spirit you have shown throughout the meeting," said Sir Cecil Weir, as he left the chair.

Mr. Arthur Mortimer halted for a moment by the Chairman, "Perhaps you may not realize it yet, sir, but this is an historic meeting," he said.

It was. That meeting led to the formation of the General Penicillin Committee of which Mr. Mortimer acted as Chairman until within a year of the end of the war, when he was succeeded by Sir Henry Dale. At a later date, Professor Raistrick was appointed as Honorary Adviser to the Ministry of Supply on Penicillin Production, in which capacity he not only gave freely of his time to assist in solving the scientific problems of manufacture, but also rendered fine services during the visits he made to the United States and Canada to study and discuss production with the scientists and manufacturers there.

The developments which sprang from that first meeting and led from the earliest penicillin factory in Great Britain to the most up-to-date factory in the world will be told in the final chapter.

CHAPTER XIII

SAVING THE WOUNDED

IT was a vivid, memorable scene on October 11, 1945, when the President of the Royal College of Surgeons in his black robe with scarlet facings walked on the platform of the lecture hall of the College in Lincoln's Inn Fields and announced to the august gathering that the Committee had reviewed the scientists of the world to find one whose outstanding work merited the award of the Lister Medal and their unanimous choice had been Sir Howard Florey, who stood beside him on the platform and to whom, with felicitous phrases, he presented the Lister Prize in the form of a cheque and the Lister Gold Medal, amid the applause of the assembly. In a gracious speech of thanks, Sir Howard told of his experiences in North Africa when he had asked the surgeons dealing with the wounded to do things not usually done in surgical practice and how loyally the surgeons had co-operated with him.

"I remember one young medical officer looking over my shoulder as I indicated to the surgeon what I wanted him to do. 'It's murder. It's murder,' the voice kept repeating in my ear. It was not pleasant" said Florey. "But the patient recovered," he added.

That young captain in the Royal Army Medical Corps was not very receptive to new ideas.

Fortunately Major-General L. T. Poole, the Director of Pathology at the War Office, was interested in penicillin from the beginning and had been in frequent contact with Professor Florey, so when it was suggested that cases might be treated in North Africa to determine the influence of penicillin upon war wounds, the War Office offered the fullest co-operation. Favourable reports of penicillin had already filtered through to London from Lieutenant-Colonel Pulvertaft in Cairo who had used the small quantity sent out in July 1942, and he and Colonel J. S. K. Boyd were convinced that "penicillin offered the best prospect of successfully clearing up the numerous chronically septic conditions met with in Base hospitals."

At last the stage was set for attempting something new in the treatment of war wounds. Production at Oxford had been going on ceaselessly to build up a small stock; the weekly brew of Kemball, Bishop went to swell the supply; the Imperial Chemical Industries were grappling with the problems of production and adding their quota to the national store, while the Therapeutic Research Corporation handed over all it had to the Penicillin Clinical Trials Committee of the Medical Research Council.

Major-General Poole wasted no time. Collecting the available penicillin, he dispatched it to North Africa with Lieutenant-Colonel Ian Fraser, who was a specialist in surgery, and Major Scott Thomson, who specialized in pathology. They reached Algiers at the end of May just after Lieutenant-General Sir Bernard Horrocks had launched his armour across Cap Bon and forced the surrender of Von Arnim and the surviving Axis forces. The calcium salt of penicillin from Oxford was packed in bulk and was relatively easy to handle and make up. The other supplies were packed in ampoules and bottles with the idea that the penicillin could be diluted in these glass containers and injected; but the ampoules and bottles were not big enough to hold the necessary water and in the end the penicillin had to be taken from them and packed in bulk. The specialists sent out from England began their clinical work on May 27, 1943, in Algiers where they selected sixteen cases of flesh wounds and eighteen cases of fractured bones. In some cases the wounds had been infected for three weeks while others had been septic for as long as four months. Sulphonamides had been used by the doctors in every known way without much effect and all the cases had become chronic. The men with flesh wounds were in fairly good shape and the local application of penicillin direct to their wounds brought good results.

It was otherwise with the men suffering from fractures. Most of them were in a bad way. Some had a high fever, others were wasted, three suffered from bedsores, others had abcesses deep down in their wounds, while many were so weak that they were unable to do anything for themselves. The results in some cases were pitiful. Flies were the curse of the African campaign. They swarmed around everything. Nothing in those days could keep them away. During operations they alighted on the instruments in the hands of the surgeons, they settled on the wounds and infected them with *Bacillus coli*, *Bacillus pyocyaneus* and *Bacillus proteus*. But they did worse things. They dropped on the wounds of the helpless patients and infested them with maggots, they extruded the minute worms into the bandages and the pests would make their way to the living flesh. It was horrible. Extra doctors were brought in, more nurses put into the wards to circumvent the flies, but it was impossible to guard each patient all the time. Directly an orderly turned his back on a patient, a fly would alight and the damage was done.

The local application of penicillin to the wounds of those patients was disappointing. But injections brought about some good recoveries, although a great deal of penicillin was required, ranging from 1,250,000 units to 1,650,000 units for each patient. A very bad case passed away under an operation, and after reviewing the results so far obtained, the specialists concluded it would be better to employ the small stocks of penicillin available, and at the same time help to conserve the supply, by using the drug on men who were newly wounded. Their judgment was fully justified, for although the drug was effective in chronic cases, its early application and administration to the newly-wounded gave penicillin a real chance to exercise its full powers.

Soon after these clinical tests started, Professor Florey arrived in North Africa with Brigadier Hugh Cairns, the Consulting Neuro-Surgeon to the Army, with a further supply of penicillin. They aimed with the co-operation of the specialists and surgeons to work out as quickly as possible the best methods of administration and the type of case on which it would be most effective. In the first flush of using this wonderful drug there was a tendency to expect too much of it. Florey was compelled to impress upon everybody that there were limits to what penicillin could do and that it was a sheer waste of the drug to use it on germs that were insensitive to penicillin. It was therefore essential to make sure that the germs infecting the patient were sensitive. This could be done only by culturing the germs and testing them against the penicillin by the ring method of Heatley. If the germs were sensitive, the surgeons could then decide on the method of administration.

It was in this field of administering penicillin that a big advance was made in the treatment of war wounds. Up to that time it was considered dangerous to stitch a wound immediately after surgical attention at a forward base hospital and it was the general rule to apply a dressing and leave the wound open to be dealt with at the base hospital. Only in exceptional cases were wounds closed immediately after wounding, and surgeons might justifiably regard any alteration of the accepted practice as something akin to murder, for to sew up an infected wound and lock up the deadly germs in the body of the patient was to run the grave risk of poisoning the patient with the toxins of the germs.

It was well for humanity that Florey went to North Africa to persuade the army surgeons to reverse their proved methods of treatment and that the surgeons had the courage to do what he demanded. Not all of them did it without misgivings and one or two expressed themselves with considerable more force than truth, as events disclosed. But it is right to say that the Oxford professor received the fullest co-operation, and in three months his knowledge inspired the medical teams in Africa to put the penicillin treatment of war wounds on a firm basis. That was the magnitude of his achievement.

The general aim had always been to give a wounded man surgical attention directly he was brought out of the line; and with the advent of penicillin this procedure was continued and a local application of penicillin was applied to the wound before the wounded man was conveyed to a forward base hospital where his wound could be given further treatment. Each wound, of course, presented a different problem. With some it was possible to dust the open wound with penicillin mixed with sulphanilamide powder before suturing it and many wounds so treated healed quickly by first intention; the flesh united in all its cellular parts and grew firmly together. In deep wounds it was essential to see that the penicillin reached every recess in order to cope with the germs and in such cases the surgeons inserted small rubber tubes to reach the bottom of the wounds and then sewed up the wound, leaving the tops of the rubber tubes to emerge through the dressing. Then it became a simple matter to instil a small quantity of penicillin into the wound every three hours by placing it in these tubes, which were withdrawn as healing advanced.

As a rule the wound was stitched so that it would not allow the solution of penicillin to run out. But evacuating the pus that collected in the wounds was a ticklish problem. And the surgeons dealing with the early cases were greatly shocked to find a nasty pink pus oozing out between the stitches of wounds. They admitted that their first tendency was to take off the dressings, but they practised restraint and found that the wounds healed just as well when the pus was present as when it was absent. This pus was caused by the *Bacillus pyocyaneus* which was not sensitive to penicillin. But the drug in dealing with the sensitive germs, enabled the defences of the body to deal with the other invading germs and so heal the wound. It was a division of labour, shared by the natural defences of the body and the penicillin which worked together in the closest harmony to destroy the germs. It sometimes happened that the penicillin dealt with all the germs right up to the walls of the wound where insensitive germs would produce the substance named penicillinase which destroyed penicillin, in which case the surgeon would inject some penicillin into a muscle from which the drug would diffuse through the body fluids to attack the boundaries of the wound from the inside and when the insensitive germs were attacked in this way from the back and front the leucocytes and defensive fluids of the body were able to vanquish them.

Day by day the medical teams groped their way toward perfecting the technique of treating war wounds with penicillin. They had their setbacks, when patients died, but their successes grew with their experience. They applied penicillin in the form of a powder, they applied it in the form of a cream, they injected it into muscles and veins, they instilled a solution into the wounds through rubber tubes at intervals of three hours, and they allowed it to drip continuously through a tube into the wound or a vein by arranging a container full of penicillin solution at the head of the bed. They treated chronic cases of infection and healed them; they treated the deadly gas gangrene with encouraging results; they dealt with compound fractures with increasing success; they treated head wounds and wounds of the brain and spinal column, improving their technique, learning all the time; they treated and cured gonorrhæa with remarkable celerity.

In three months of unremitting scientific investigation Professor Florey and Brigadier Cairns and all the other specialists and medical officers who co-operated with them not only confirmed that penicillin was one of the most remarkable drugs so far discovered, but they initiated methods of treatment, fixed the dosage and period of administration and reduced the suffering of the wounded by days and weeks—in most cases the wounded were convalescent in half the time. All this meant that men were saved who would otherwise have died and it is obvious that penicillin played its part in reducing the mortality among the wounded in this war to the lowest ever known.

These clinical trials of penicillin carried out in North Africa justified the British Government in giving priority to the production of penicillin as a war-winning measure. But it must not be thought that all the difficulties of production were banished at the mere edict of the Government. Far from it. They persisted and still persist, despite the care exercised in countering them. Nevertheless penicillin production was stepped up wherever possible and while the quantity tended to increase, it still remained woefully meagre.

In due course the fine work rendered to the fighting services was duplicated for the war workers by Dr. Ethel Florey and Dr. R. E. O. Williams in the Birmingham accident hospital where they selected 212 cases of hand infections. Of these, 102 cases were treated in the normal manner and 110 were treated with penicillin which overcame the infection in a week, while the other cases were still septic. The penicillin cases were dressed with one thousand units once a day for five days, and their hands healed more quickly and they could use them much better than the patients treated by ordinary methods. In thirty-five cases the penicillin patients were able to resume work thirty days before any controls—which means that if they earned fifteen shillings a day the penicillin put over £750 in their pay packets.

Research workers are still studying penicillin all over the world and the bare titles of the scientific papers written on the subject would fill dozens of pages of this book. Each paper deals with some peculiarity or some mystery of this magic drug and yet no doubt there remains much to be learned about the action of penicillin, despite the intensive work on the subject.

The remarkable qualities of the drug have exceeded the anticipation of Fleming who set some of them down so clearly in his first paper in which he told of his experiments with something which he named penicillin. He stated then that it was bactericidal because he could see by his original plate that it possessed the power to destroy the sensitive germs. The Oxford team differed on this point, but other research workers proved Fleming to be right. Professor Bigger furnished the evidence which proved that penicillin did in fact kill off the staphylococci. Bigger found that among millions of staphylococci were a few that differed slightly from the others— these variants were not more than one in a million. But they survived a lethal dose of penicillin and developed new colonies of cocci which the scientist named persisters, with which he carried out a number of interesting experiments. The main fact which emerged was that penicillin killed the bacteria only when they were splitting up and dividing, or when the germs were giving birth to new germs.

While Professor Bigger was conducting these researches, Dr. E. W. Todd, who was present when Fleming discovered the mould growing on the agar plate, carried out some experiments which proved that penicillin possessed the power to dissolve pneumococci and staphylococci, particularly when the germs were young and multiplying actively, and he suggested in his paper published in the *Lancet* in January, 1945, that bacteriostasis and bactericidal action

and bacteriolysis were different stages of a single process. Three
American scientists, G. L. Hobby, K. Meyer and E. Chaffee proved
in 1942 that penicillin was most fatal to sensitive germs when they
were most actively multiplying, and they grew Fleming's mould on a
variation of the chemical medium first used by Raistrick for this
specific purpose.

It is generally well known that a man can develop a high degree
of immunity against the deadliest poison. By taking a minute dose
of the poison that is insufficient to do any harm, the defences of the
body may be stimulated against the poison, and by gradually increasing the doses of poison the defences of the body can be so
stimulated and strengthened that the poison is no longer poisonous
to the man. He has developed immunity against it. That is what
happens to drug addicts and that was why De Quincey was able to
take doses of opium strong enough to kill several men.

It was a peculiar thing that unusual strains of the cocci that were
normally most sensitive to penicillin and succumbed at the touch of
it were discovered in North Africa. These unusual strains were
hardly affected by penicillin at all. They were relatively insensitive
to it, or immune from it.

Naturally enough, scientists sought to discover what happened to
germs after repeated doses of penicillin. Twenty years ago I formulated the theory that bacteria were subject to the same laws of
immunity as human beings—only to find that Ehrlich had formulated a similar theory long before me. Fleming himself took a
micrococcus that was very sensitive to lysozyme and by selecting
cocci that showed some resistance to the lysozyme and subjecting
them to increasing doses of this ferment he produced a strain of
micrococcus against which lysozyme was quite powerless. Having
endowed the micrococcus with this power, Fleming tried to take it
away. But he could not do so. After growing it in ordinary media
for generation after generation for nine months, the descendants of
the micrococcus were still unaffected by lysozyme, which rather
suggested that Fleming had endowed the strain with a new
characteristic.

Working on similar lines in America, C. M. McKee and G. Rake
took a pneumococcus which could withstand a small dose of three-
hundredths of a unit of penicillin and from it produced a strain in
fifty-five generations that could withstand a dose of penicillin thirty-
two times as strong, and when they tried to deprive the coccus of
this resistance by growing it in ordinary blood broth they found

that the coccus after thirty-two subcultures was still able to resist penicillin. Other American scientists obtained resistant strains of pneumococci by passing them through mice treated with penicillin, but they could not rob the germs of this new power by passing them through ordinary mice. Again another scientist cultured an immune strain of staphylococci by growing them for one generation after another in over a hundred test tubes. Transferring them to some veal agar, he stored them in the refrigerator for three months and found they could still resist penicillin.

Dr. E. W. Todd and his colleagues G. S. Turner and E. G. W. Drew in their desire to increase our knowledge of how germs behaved after repeated doses of penicillin took the strain of staphylococcus known as the Oxford Strain H, because it was used to test the strength of the penicillin produced at Oxford, and carried out a series of experiments. At the start of their first experiment the germ was so vulnerable that it could not grow in a weak solution of six-hundredths of a unit of penicillin, but after selecting the most resistant strain and culturing it twenty-seven times to produce twenty-seven generations they produced a strain that would grow in one hundred and sixty units of penicillin. These germs were unharmed by a dose three thousand times as strong as the dose which was fatal to their forbears. Having attained this high degree of immunity in the staphylococci, Dr. Todd and his colleagues sought to take from the germs the characteristic with which they had endowed them. They grew a new generation every day on a tryptic digest broth that contained no penicillin. In a week the cocci could not grow in a hundred units of penicillin, although they could grow in fifty units; and in thirty-six generations the staphylococci had lost nearly all their remarkable resistance, for it needed only twelve-hundredths of a unit of penicillin to prevent them from growing. This was still double the resistance of the original strain, which was prevented from growing by six-hundredths of a unit.

They cultured another strain that grew in two hundred and fifty units of penicillin; a third that flourished in three hundred and twenty units, in other words these germs could tolerate doses of penicillin over five-thousand times as strong as that which was fatal to their progenitors. It was rather remarkable. Yet by growing a new generation on agar without penicillin every day for twenty-eight days, this strong immunity was destroyed and the staphylococcus would not grow in six-tenths of a unit of penicillin, although it would just grow in five-tenths of a unit. That tiny difference of one-tenth of a unit meant life or death to the staphylococcus.

These researches suggest that the scientist can endow the pneumococcus with an immunity against penicillin which remains fixed and cannot be taken away, and that he can also furnish the staphylococcus with an immunity of resistance which he can destroy as easily as it was created. Why the two germs should behave so differently is rather puzzling and no one at present knows the answer. Other germs have been cultured to resist the sulphonamides and here again the resistance has remained fixed. It makes the behaviour of the staphylococcus more puzzling than ever. One interesting fact emerged from these experiments. In endowing the staphylococci with resistance, it was noted that a gradual change was wrought in their appearance, and the germs which showed the greatest difference to the original strain showed the greatest resistance to penicillin, so it looked as though Dr. Todd and his colleagues had bred an entirely new race of germs which soon reverted to type. An analogy may be found in the fields where by selection alone a skilled Sussex cultivator produced a breed of wheat which gave a much higher yield than his original wheat; yet when this same high-yielding wheat was planted in the ordinary way for a year or two it soon reverted to type and gave a smaller yield than at the start of the experiment. In changing the appearance of the germs by treating them with penicillin, Dr. Todd recalled the earlier work at Oxford of Professor Gardner who not only cultured the remarkable giant forms of germs, but who was the first to discover that the staphylococcus could acquire a resistance against penicillin.

The magic of penicillin is something which seems to oppose many theories and confound all pedants. The potency of pure penicillin is indeed so great that the human mind can no more grasp it than it can grasp the conception of eternal space or the distance of the stars from the earth. Tell the average man that he is looking at a star which ceased to exist millions of years ago and he will think you are talking nonsense. Yet it is none the less true. We delude ourselves that we see a star, when what we see is the light given off by that star millions of years ago, light that is still travelling to this earth at the rate of 186,000 miles a second and impinging on our eyes after the star, the source of the light, has died out. The astronomers talk glibly of light-years, meaning the distance that a ray of light can travel at a velocity of 186,000 miles a second in a year, but even their minds are not sufficiently developed to have a true conception of what it means; nor can we comprehend what it means in terms of potency to say that one part of penicillin in one hundred millions will stop the growth of sensitive germs.

The sulphonamides tend to lose their potency in the presence of pus; but penicillin carries on its beneficent work even when it is overwhelmed with pus; it acts just as surely against the germs which are sensitive and destroys them. This is a wonderful quality.

On the other hand the drug is so liable to be destroyed by different things such as heat, numerous metals and so many air-borne bacteria that a slight puff of air may banish all the magic power of penicillin. It diffuses with astonishing ease through the skin of the mould into the medium, and when amyl acetate is mixed with the medium the penicillin automatically passes from the medium into the amyl acetate; and if alkaline water is mixed with amyl acetate the penicillin just as naturally parts company with the amyl acetate and enters the water. This power of diffusion, of dissolving, of passing from one solvent into another was the power which enabled the Oxford scientists to give penicillin to humanity.

It follows that if such a substance be reduced to a powder, that powder will also possess the same affinity for water and the same facility for dissolving in it. The salt of penicillin was indeed so absorbent that directly a pinch of it was exposed to the air, it absorbed the moisture from the atmosphere and in a short time lost its potency. This was another drawback against which the scientists had to guard in handling and administering the salt of penicillin. Happily the calcium salt of penicillin proved to be more stable in this respect and it came to be more widely used for local application in the form of dusting and other local methods; while the sodium salt of penicillin was generally used for injections.

Thus it came about that by October, 1943, the efficacy of penicillin was fully established by all those doctors, in uniform and out, who had been privileged to play their great part in the clinical trials on the battlefields of North Africa.

In his Report on the Operations in North-West Europe from June 6, 1944, to May 5, 1945, published on September 4, 1946, Field Marshal The Viscount Montgomery of Alamein ultimately summed up the importance of penicillin in the war by writing: "The healing of war wounds has been revolutionized by the use of penicillin. Many men who in the last war would have been permanent invalids were fit and ready to go back to the line within a month of being wounded."

CHAPTER XIV

THE CRYSTALS ARE FOUND

At last we can deal with the work of the crystallographers who, notwithstanding that they and their science are little known, kept Dr. Chain and Dr. Abraham informed of the progress they were making toward the determination of the structure of penicillin. It was difficult work, so involved in complex calculations that Dr. Heatley mentioned quietly that he did not understand it.

This work of extreme delicacy and intricacy, which consisted of the analysis of crystals by X-rays, was accomplished by a young scientist, Mrs. Dorothy Hodgkin, whose brilliant papers under her maiden name of Crowfoot won for her a place as one of the outstanding crystallographers in England, and she and her chief assistant, Mrs. Barbara Rogers, toiled like slaves of the lamp to reveal the inner mysteries of penicillin.

"The work of Mrs. Hodgkin helped our work forward and speeded it up by months," said Dr. Abraham. "She could tell almost at a glance what we had got and what we had not got."

To learn something of this abstruse science which played so important a part in the elucidation of the chemical structure of penicillin, I visited Mrs. Hodgkin at her laboratory in Oxford one sunny afternoon and was translated in a flash to the medieval atmosphere of the old alchemists. Grisly skeletons of prehistoric mammoths towered overhead; the black and red tiles underfoot were worn into undulations by countless feet as I followed my guide to a massive oak Gothic door strapped with black iron hinges and studded with big black nails, at the back of the gallery beside these ancient bones. It was rather eerie.

I entered a gloomy room with a long table occupying the centre; along the left wall was a range of glass-doored cupboards with shelves stacked full of cardboard boxes containing half-plate negatives; over in the right-hand corner was a cabinet about two feet high with an opal glass top about twelve inches wide by eighteen inches long. Some ordinary bent wood chairs had seen much wear. Books and papers were scattered around. The dingy room was lit by windows at the far end along which ran a worn wooden working bench, between which and the end of the cupboard on the left wall was tucked away a small table whereon Mrs. Hodgkin was working in the most favourable light. She was young, about five feet five inches tall, clad in a brown corduroy jerkin resembling the battle blouse of a soldier, a short skirt of turquoise homespun, beige stockings on her legs and stout brown shoes on her feet. She had very blue eyes, a strong roman nose and firm mouth, fluffy flaxen hair and a healthy complexion which scorned powder and paint, and to me she bore a marked resemblance in a feminine way to Lawrence of Arabia. Her handshake was firm and friendly, and she was as modest and unassuming as she was clever. She had patience and lucidity in explaining highly technical matters, and above all she had the fairness and generosity to give full credit to those associated with her in the work. Her mind was orderly. She marshalled her facts as neatly as the sergeant drills a well-trained squad on the barrack square and it made me wonder whether the study of a mass of meticulous detail by the scientist had created the orderly mind or nature's gift of an orderly mind had created the scientist.

On the bench by the window was a baseboard into which were thrust a number of metal rods about the size of a thick knitting needle in diameter, and varying in length from about eight to eighteen inches. Placed irregularly without apparent geometrical design, each rod held a cork disc, resembling a tap washer, of various colours such as black, green, blue, red or yellow. Some of these discs were high up on the long rods, others were half way down the short rods, but so far as I could see in a casual scrutiny no two were actually on the same plane, but all were resting at different levels on their supporting rods. It looked rather like one of the games that children play in the kindergarten.

Mrs. Hodgkin smiled at my puzzled glance.

"That is the way we visualize a molecule of penicillin. That is how we judge it to be from our X-ray analysis."

Each disc on its rod represented an atom of the molecule, and each colour represented an element such as nitrogen, oxygen, hydrogen and so on, and to any scientist familiar with the subject this model gave at sight all the information that was known. We are so in the habit of regarding a sugar crystal as being quite solid that it is not easy to realize that it is actually as full of holes as a parmesan cheese in which the big holes are so visible that no one would think of denying their existence. Now a single crystal of sugar is made up of molecules or ions that are not packed solidly together at all. A good deal of space lies between them, as it does when you take some steel ball bearings and pack them as close together as you possibly can. Although they make contact with each other at particular points, open spaces remain between the points that are touching. This holds true whether it be a crystal of snow, of salt, of sugar or of penicillin. What appears to be solid to the human eye is in fact full of holes which are just as invisible as are the molecules or ions of which the crystal is formed. The crystallographer explores these realms of the infinitely small where so-called solid matter is disintegrated into its ultimate atoms and molecules and ions.

These molecules forming a crystal of penicillin are far too small ever to be detected by ordinary light which travels to the earth in a series of waves. These light waves are so big by comparison that the atoms remain unseen in the dark spaces between the waves, just as a man may be overlooked who stands under the beam of a searchlight which is illuminating a church tower two miles away. The light shines over his head and he remains in darkness. To see anything so small as the atoms of the different elements of which a crystal of penicillin is formed, the waves of light must be small enough to impinge on these atoms and not shine over them. And X-rays consist of waves of light short enough to enable the atom to be explored, although the scientist never actually sees, in the accepted sense, the atoms at all. What is seen is the shadowy, but none the less clear, evidence registered by the atom itself under the light of the X-rays.

When Mrs. Hodgkin photographed a crystal of penicillin by X-rays, the light passing through the crystal was scattered by the various atoms on which it impinged, in scientific terms the light was diffracted, and these diffracted beams made a series of tiny dots on the developed negative. A crystal photographed in this way reproduced a distinct pattern. It was its own pattern and nothing else in the whole of nature could reproduce a pattern exactly like it. The dots it made fell in certain positions on the film and every other crystal of a similar kind photographed from exactly the same angle would make a similar pattern with the dots falling exactly in the same places so that two photographs could be superimposed and if examined under a strong back light would appear as one. As the printer would say, they would register perfectly. This being so, it follows that if the crystallographer found in the pattern a dot too many or a dot too few, or of markedly different intensity, it was proof that the substance under analysis was not exactly the same as the known substance. It may have been very, very like, but there must have been a molecular variation which made it slightly different chemically. It is just as impossible for a crystal of penicillin to produce a pattern like that produced by a crystal of tartaric acid as it is for a photograph of a chair to develop into a photograph of an elephant. No one would mistake a photograph of an elephant for an armchair, because the distinctions are so great as to be recognized by all; and to the highly-trained crystallographer the patterns made by different crystals are just as distinctive.

An additional aid is the spectrum analysis which enables a scientist to identify all the known elements. A burning element, viewed through the spectroscope, forms a series of bands of light, of different colours, on the spectrum, with black spaces in between; the bands may be a combination of wide and narrow bands with lines of light as fine as hairs, and they may be red, blue, green, violet, orange or yellow or combinations and variations of the known colours. The modern spectroscope used for reflecting the beam of light from the burning element on to the screen of ground glass is a concave plate of bronze engraved with fine lines so close together that it is difficult to detect them with the naked eye. The lines are automatically cut by a diamond point which may move up and down the bronze plate without ceasing day or night for a week. After each line is cut, the diamond point is automatically moved forward for the almost imperceptible space of a twenty-thousandth of an inch. The beam of light impinging on the spectroscope is broken up by these engraved lines and reflected upon the screen in the form of bands. The spectrum or pattern made by every element so far discovered is on record and it is rather remarkable that an unusual line in a spectrum led to the discovery of helium in the sun a generation before it was discovered on the earth.

The longest ray of light that can be seen by the human eye is a red ray one 32,000th of an inch long, but there are red rays twice this length which cannot be seen. At the other end of the scale the shortest visible ray is the violet ray one 62,850th of an inch in length, or roughly half the length of the longest red ray we can see. But the X-rays with which Mrs. Hodgkin discovered the molecular make-up of penicillin were rays of light only a sixty-one-millionth of an inch long and these invisible rays were small enough to impinge on the exceedingly small molecules forming the crystal.

"In addition to classical crystallographic methods, we mainly used X-ray methods," she said. "In the essential process we took diffraction photographs of the crystalline products. The patterns observed were related to the arrangement of the atoms in the crystals and it was possible by a laborious process to work out in about eighteen months what was the specific arrangement of atoms which would give the diffraction effects we had observed. The arrangement was then known to be very close to that of the atoms in the molecule of penicillin." Here again it was a question of team work, for a number of mathematicians were called upon to lend their aid and great help was obtained from some scientific computing machines controlled by the Government as well as from a commercial company known as the Scientific Computing Service. It was the importance of penicillin which made these labours worth while.

Another scientist who greatly helped the work was Mr. C. W. Bunn of the Imperial Chemical Industries at Northwich who, acting on a suggestion made by Sir Lawrence Bragg, one of the world's most famous crystallographers, developed a special camera known as the Fly's Eye Camera. This device was essentially a multiple pinhole camera which reproduced a number of times over in a regular array the pattern that was photographed through it. This multiple pattern could be made to give diffraction effects with visible light, and possible atomic patterns could be tested to see whether they were capable of giving diffraction effects similar to those observed by X-rays. This device saved much time in the analysis of penicillin by cutting down the number of calculations needed.

"We sent up a lot of data to Bunn for him to try out, and he worked out the pattern for the sodium salt of penicillin and we worked out the patterns for the potassium and rubidium salts. The sodium salt and the potassium salt were sent to us from the United States by the two chemical firms of Squibb and Merck, while the rubidium salt came from the Imperial Chemical Industries at Trafford Park, Manchester," remarked Mrs. Hodgkin.

At that time, in the summer of 1945, she was still working on penicillin and did not expect to complete her computations for two months.

As we know, the ultimate goal of Chain and Abraham was to obtain penicillin in the form of pure crystals—that is the aim of all biochemists and chemists when they discover a new substance— but although they tried several times to crystallize out the purest form of calcium salt of penicillin then available, they failed to obtain the crystals. Mrs. Hodgkin, who is an adept at growing crystals, also worked with a barium salt without success. In fact, the penicillin was too impure, and Mrs. Hodgkin knew that this was why she could not obtain the pure crystals. She did not worry. Each week Chain and Abraham were obtaining penicillin in a purer form and she felt sure it would be a simple matter to obtain the crystals from the highly-purified penicillin that would be ready later on.

Then one Saturday the news came through that the American scientists had obtained the crystals from the sodium salt of penicillin. "Directly I heard that the workers in the United States had managed to secure the crystal form, I knew we could do the same," remarked Mrs. Hodgkin.

She went across to the School of Pathology to discuss the matter with Chain and Abraham, who had now decided to try to crystallize the sodium salt of their own purest preparation. "Will you give me some of the sodium salt so that I can try it myself?" she asked.

"I am starting to make it at once," said Dr. Abraham, who thereupon went to the refrigerator and took out a small quantity of the purest barium salt of the Oxford penicillin, P.1, and prepared to change it into sodium salt by what he would call a simple chemical conversion. Making the barium salt into a solution in water, he added to it the desired quantity of sodium sulphate. As the barium sulphate was insoluble, this deposited on the bottom of the glass vessel while the remaining solution of penicillin then contained sodium in the place of the barium originally present. This was made intensely cold and dried in a vacuum, as already explained, and the result was an uncrystallized powder of the sodium salt of penicillin. It was very little, about two milligrammes, but it was sufficient for the purpose. Passing some on to Mrs. Hodgkin, Dr. Abraham began the task of crystallizing his portion of the pale yellow powder, trying, among other things, the addition of acetone to make the crystals grow out of the solution; but all his efforts were futile.

Meanwhile Mrs. Hodgkin was grappling with the same task in her own laboratory a little distance away. Dissolving some of the sodium salt, she attempted to precipitate it in the usual way by adding another liquid to start the crystals forming. The normal reaction did not occur. The crystals refused to form. The stubborn penicillin clung tenaciously to its secret. She experimented with one thing after another throughout the Sunday. All the tricks known to crystallographers were tried in vain.

Very tired and disappointed at her lack of success, Mrs. Hodgkin left her bench on Sunday evening and went home. She returned to her laboratory on the Monday morning to try again. Going to her bench, she picked up a glass slide on which she had left a spot of the sodium salt overnight. She could hardly believe her eyes. There on the slide were the perfect crystals of sodium salt of penicillin. The penicillin had actually formed its own crystals while she was asleep.

"It was rather funny," she said, with a smile.

To the very end penicillin lived up to its reputation of acting in an unpredictable manner.

In a flash the scientist knew what had happened. The pinch of sodium salt had simply absorbed the moisture from the atmosphere until it liquefied and then it had crystallized out. It was as easy as that.

The crystallization of penicillin in this way might easily have happened some time before. The fact that it did not, proves how precious was each atom of penicillin to the Oxford workers and how carefully they took care of it. We know full well that if the sodium salt of penicillin is exposed to the air it absorbs the moisture from the atmosphere and loses its potency. That was the thing above all others that the Oxford workers were keen to guard against. They did not want to expend their efforts to obtain a useless yellow powder. The consequence was that they dried it and kept it very dry and thus maintained most rigidly the very conditions that were antagonistic to the formation of the crystals.

For the very reason that the calcium salt was easier to handle and not so liable to lose its potency when exposed to the atmosphere, the Oxford workers used it in all their former attempts to obtain penicillin in crystal form. They failed. And no one has yet succeeded in crystallizing the calcium salt. It ought to form crystals, but it does not. Nobody at Oxford knows the reason why. That is another peculiarity of penicillin.

Hurrying off happily to the School of Pathology, Mrs. Hodgkin went to the laboratory of Dr. Abraham. "I've got the crystals," she said, and told him all about it.

"If you've got them, I must have them, too," he replied. Walking over to his bench, he picked up a slide on which he had left a trace of the sodium salt. There were the crystals, most beautifully formed. It really was rather amusing, as though penicillin were playing a practical joke on them.

Without delay, Mrs. Hodgkin put on the X-Rays to take a photograph of a crystal and was able to discover the cell dimensions of the sodium salt. Fortunately Dr. Coghill, who was visiting Oxford from Peoria at that time, was just about to return to the United States, so the technical details were given to him to see if they agreed with the cell dimensions of the sodium salt crystallized in the United States.

That was a question which the scientists of the United States could not answer, because the Oxford workers were so far in advance that no one in the United States was working with X-rays on penicillin. However, the Oxford scientists, acting as ever in the interests of humanity, sent particulars of this branch of the work out to the United States to enable the American scientists to perform their own X-ray analyses.

A month or two later Sir Robert Robinson who was working on the secret chemical problems of penicillin in the Dyson Perrins Laboratory at Oxford, returned with the latest information from the United States and then it was realized that the penicillin produced in the United States was different to the penicillin produced in Oxford.

Thus it transpired that although the American scientists were the first to crystallize the American penicillin, known as P.2, the Oxford scientists who first gave penicillin to the world, were the first to obtain the Oxford penicillin, known as P.1, in crystal form. It is possible that the workers of the Imperial Chemical Industries may have observed crystals in some of their preparations earlier, although they did not definitely identify them.

Explaining how the spacing of the atoms in the molecule causes the minute black spots which form the pattern on the X-ray photograph, Mrs. Hodgkin said: "What we observe in these arrangements of the dots are the diffraction effects and from these, in the final stage of our analysis, we can calculate a pattern of electron densities. And what we do in the end is to plot them on a contour map."

She took out a folder and produced a sheet of paper printed with small blue squares on which was ruled in ink a square, roughly eight inches by eight. Within this square were marked hundreds of groups of tiny numbers in red ink. There were 900 groups in all and I noticed that the figures 37 recurred in various parts. Each group of figures entailed a sum of addition and subtraction to arrive at the right answer and then it was marked in its correct place on the map which revealed to the crystallographer all that was known about the section of the crystal under examination. Many such maps must be made to cover the whole crystal. The map bore a strong resemblance to an ordinary contour map, with a series of whorls and whirls like the magnified lines on the skin of the ball of the thumb and all about these whirling lines occurred these groups of figures which to the specialist meant so much and to the average man nothing at all, because he could not understand them—which was not surprising, considering that some of the scientists who solved the problems of penicillin were unable to comprehend this intricate scientific work which helped them in their task.

"Would you care to see where we take the photographs?" Mrs. Hodgkin asked, and led me past the skeleton down some stairs into a dungeon-like place that was more than ever like the den of an ancient alchemist. A little light filtered down from a small window high upon the wall just under the ceiling and beneath this window was a platform connected with the lower floor by a ladder. In the left corner of the place was a big square metal cabinet with a black pipe running from the side of the room to a black object, shaped not unlike a rugby football which hung over the top of the cabinet. It was below this black spheroid which emitted the X-rays that the crystals were placed to be photographed.

Opening a small door in the wall, Mrs. Hodgkin went down a few brick steps into an inner dungeon devoid of light and emerged with a tin cigarette box in her hand. It was padded with cotton wool and full of little phials, labelled with the names of the crystals they contained. "I keep the penicillin in the refrigerator," she explained, and took out a phial with two or three layers of cellophane over the mouth of it. "These are penicillin crystals," she said. "There is about a milligramme."

I saw a sprinkle of what appeared to be white powder round the sides of the tube. Then she picked out another tube in which she was growing crystals, and I observed the crystals forming in the misty moisture on the sides of the tube. Replacing the penicillin crystals in the box, she climbed the ladder to the upper staging. I followed and found her removing the cover from a microscope.

"We can use the smallest quantity for identification. I can select one crystal at a time for analytical purposes. We take the photographs while the crystal turns and the camera slides up and down, and when the photographs are ready we take one line of dots at a time to fix the identity," she remarked.

Carefully wiping a glass slide, she cleaned a needle and, inserting it in the phial, took out a few of the penicillin crystals on the point. Placing the crystals on the slide, she put the slide on the stage of the microscope, switched on the light and, adjusting the focus to make sure that all was well, stood aside. "Would you care to see them?"

Making the necessary adjustment to suit my own sight, I looked down the eyepiece and saw the crystals of penicillin lying criss-cross like needles against the light ground. Noticing one crystal that was apparently marked by two or three dark spots, and wondering what these were, I readjusted the microscope to bring the crystal into proper focus and at once saw that the dark spots were other crystals lying at right angles out of focus across the top of the first crystal. After further adjustments of the microscope, I viewed the crystals under polarized light. They were very beautiful and quite fairy-like, shimmering against the background like needles of the clearest glass.

These long, sharp crystals were the purest form of a chemical produced for unknown ages by a lowly mould that was first discovered on some decaying hyssop in Norway by Westling. Countless men and women have trampled the tiny fungus into the soil without being aware of its existence; others, seeing it, regarded it as a blight. And since the dim and distant past when a miracle conjured up on earth the first minute filaments of mycelium that bore the spores which were the beginning of the whole race of *Penicillium notatum*, no one could prove that this tiny fungus possessed the magical power of saving human life until the secret was revealed by those gifted scientists who formed the Oxford team.

What is the exact manner in which this mould produces the penicillin? That is the mystery. To say that the fungus produces penicillin in the medium is perfectly accurate, but much too general to serve for the specific scientific statement I desired to make.

"Can you tell me the exact way in which the mould creates the penicillin?" I asked Sir Alexander Fleming.

He smiled. "We do not know," he replied.

I asked Professor Raistrick. "Nobody knows," he answered.

I asked Dr. Chain and he could not tell me, so one vital fact still remains to be discovered in connection with penicillin.

What is penicillin? How is it made? These simple questions raised most complex issues. I questioned whether the penicillin was a waste product of the mould that was comparable with the waste products of the human body and learned that it was not. Did the mould deposit something in the medium which combined with some of the chemicals in the medium to form penicillin? Here again the answer was "no." Because the penicillin can be detected in the medium when the mould begins to blossom and spore and the medium changes to a yellow colour, I wondered if the penicillin was the product of the pollen which the mould dropped into the medium; but here again the answer was "no." I queried whether the penicillin was produced by the decay of the mould as it passed from the reproductive stage to old age, and was assured that it was not a product of decay. Was it some vital substance, resembling human hormones, which enabled the mould to blossom and fruit and reproduce its kind? And here again we can only say that we do not know.

Some germs defend themselves from attack by emitting a poison with which they seek to destroy their attackers. This form of poison is known as an exotoxin, because it is a defensive product which manifests outside the germ, comparable in one way to the ink discharged by an octopus that fears attack. I wondered if penicillin were similar to an exotoxin. This lowly mould grows in the soil which harbours a very mixed population of moulds, bacteria and protozoa, some of which destroy the mould as well as the penicillin which it creates. In the course of long ages it is likely that the mould has been forced to produce some active defence against its enemies in order to survive. And this defence may be penicillin, although there is no definite evidence on the point at all. It is possible that the mould in the course of time produces this defensive substance in the normal way quite automatically and it may still go on producing it automatically in the medium although the medium contains nothing harmful to the mould. Scientific proof of this is entirely lacking, but the theory remains.

The most we can say of penicillin and how it is produced is that it is a product of metabolism. The mould absorbs from the medium all that is necessary to sustain life and in the act of digesting its food and transforming it into the cells which build up into new mycelium and flowers and spores, a chemical reaction takes place inside the mycelium to form penicillin. There is no doubt that this magic substance is created inside the delicate filaments forming the organism of the mould. And penicillin is of such low molecular weight that it seeps out of the protoplasm of the organism through the skin of the mycelium and into the medium as easily as perspiration pours through the sweat glands in the human skin.

Never since the world began was the wonderful substance produced by this humble mould seen until recently by human eye as I saw it under the microscope in that cellar of Oxford University in the form of the most beautiful crystals, gleaming triumphantly against the black ground from which science had dragged them into the light of day by the sheer force of the human mind.

"They are lovely," I said.

Replacing the cover on the microscope, Mrs. Hodgkin went down the steps to the floor below and opened one of two boxes of negatives to find some special X-ray photographs. "They must be upstairs," she said, so I followed her past the skeletons and waited in her laboratory where she opened a box or two and took out several half-plate films, protected with cellophane covers to prevent them from being scratched or damaged in handling.

Going to the cabinet in the corner of the room, she touched a switch to illuminate the opal glass top from below, then she placed some of the X-ray photographs on the glass and I saw the ruled lines of the grating with a pattern of black dots which told her some of the secrets of penicillin and which were to me only a series of dots. Then she placed on the illuminated glass two more photographs with a dark spot in the centre and a series of shadow rings all round. They resembled the haloes with which the moon is sometimes surrounded, or the photographs of the sun taken in the arctic with a series of haloes. These were the two photographs of the Oxford penicillin, P.1 and the American penicillin, P.2. The rings differed slightly, and these two historic photographs showing the variation provided unchallengeable evidence which proved beyond doubt that the American penicillin was different to the original penicillin obtained in Oxford. I may mention that the penicillins now known in Great Britain under the numbers of P.1, P.2 and P.3 are described in the United States as P.F, P.G and P.X, and at the time of writing at least four, and probably five, different penicillins have been isolated.

CHAPTER XV

THE FINAL PHASE

SIR CECIL WEIR's historical meeting on September 25, 1942, to launch the production of penicillin under Government control was the first comprehensive move in Great Britain toward making penicillin available on a big scale. The original papers on penicillin by the Oxford scientists had already started a number of scientists experimenting with the mould in the laboratories of the universities. Nor were the foremost chemical manufacturers in the country far behind, for most of them had been to Oxford to see what was being done and as early as October, 1941, five of them, May and Baker, the Glaxo Laboratories, the Wellcome Foundation, British Drug Houses and Boots had combined to form the Therapeutic Research Corporation so that they could jointly investigate penicillin by pooling their knowledge. The result was that these firms and others like the Imperial Chemical Industries were already engaged upon researches which were producing small yields of penicillin, while the technical staff of Kemball, Bishop and Company had overcome the difficulties of growing the mould by their open-tray method and had delivered their first brew to Oxford fourteen days before Sir Cecil Weir called his conference,

But while everyone present was anxious to work together for the common good, it took time to resolve the many questions involved. Eventually a satisfactory basis for a united effort was reached, and by the late spring of 1943 many of the difficulties inherent in a new organization were being overcome, the spirit of co-operation between scientists and chemical manufacturers was strengthening and the interchange of knowledge became more than a pious hope and began to take place freely among the British workers as well as those of the United States.

At that time every factory in Great Britain was working in top gear on war contracts; the garages and workshops tucked away in back streets all over the land were humming with machinery; sleepy little workshops on many a village green that used to service an odd car or two in pre-war days doubled and trebled and quadrupled in size while in place of the odd man who used to laze about with a cigarette hanging from his mouth there were battalions of buxom girls in slacks who manipulated lathes and presses and beat metal

OPPOSITE: *Operators in the Glaxo penicillin plant at Watford withdrawing culture flasks from the autoclave in which they were sterilized under steam pressure for half an hour to destroy all bacteria.*

sheets into all sorts of shapes as though they had been doing it all their lives. They toiled for England and in many cases handled wages which surpassed their wildest imaginings.

It was rare to find a bench or lathe which was not busy on some sub-contract to help the war effort. To start something new in such conditions was not easy and, in view of the obstacles that were surmounted before penicillin could be produced at Oxford, it would have been rather surprising if everything had gone like clockwork. That hitches and delays were bound to occur is obvious; but their cramping effects were known only to the inner official circle, for the new project from its inception was veiled in secrecy and no hint of what was afoot was allowed to appear in the press. The officials charged with the onerous task of producing penicillin struggled in a sea of difficulties that threatened at times to swamp them. They had to decide the method of production, how much penicillin would be required, where they could find firms to make the special apparatus that would be needed, where they could obtain the raw materials for the huge quantities of medium, the chemical firms who were prepared to undertake the task, the type of factory to be built and where such factories ought to be located. All sorts of priorities were battling fiercely for labour and materials when penicillin joined in the fray.

On the other side of the Atlantic, the United States were immune from the ravages of war even after they joined in the fight. They were far removed from danger. The American people did not know the dread sound of German bombers in the sky; they were not suddenly engulfed in flames and crushed to death by buildings falling upon them. They lived a more or less normal existence, untroubled by shortages of food or anything else. The American Government did not cut the tops off men's socks or the turn-ups from their trousers; they did not condemn the American women to go bare-legged because there were no coupons to buy stockings nor stockings in the shops if the coupons existed. Little more than half the American factories and workers were engaged on war work and the rest were still busy supplying civilian needs, with the consequence that the American chemical manufacturers were able to devote every attention to the problems of penicillin while the engineers and factories were available to build the necessary chemical plant when it was wanted. Yet these obvious advantages did not enable Americans to escape the multitude of difficulties that were inseparable from the production of penicillin.

OPPOSITE: *A technical expert at the control-panel of the freeze-drying plant at the Glaxo laboratory at Greenford, where the penicillin fluid made at their other laboratories was brought to be dried.*

The visit of Florey and Heatley to the United States was indeed fruitful, for soon afterwards the Office of Scientific Research and Development in Washington called a conference of all the manufacturers interested in penicillin, and eventually twenty-one firms signed contracts with the Government agreeing to pool their knowledge and discoveries, while on their part the United States Government agreed to buy the whole production of penicillin at a fixed price. The money invested in penicillin production to-day in the United States probably amounts to about £5,000,000. As long ago as the early months of 1944 the production was touching 200,000 mega units a month, by which time, owing to the more favourable conditions, the American producers had largely overcome the worst of their troubles and the earlier surface culture plants were being superseded by deep culture production in tanks.

That Dr. Coghill was thinking in advance of the times was apparent when he asked Professor Florey at their first interview in July, 1941, whether the mould could be grown in deep culture. The researches carried out in Peoria proved that deep culture was possible, whereupon the scientists and chemical engineers in some of the big pharmaceutical laboratories successfully attained this final goal. I believe that by the middle of 1943, when surface culture plants yet to be built were still being planned in Great Britain, the firms of Chas. Pfizer and Company, Merck and Company and E. R. Squibb and Sons were preparing to abandon their surface culture plants and starting to produce penicillin by the new deep fermentation process, so they must have been working on these problems at an early date to begin production so soon. By the autumn of 1944 most of the remaining American producers were closing down surface culture and switching over to the deep fermentation process; and it is noteworthy that by the summer of 1946 Chas. Pfizer alone was producing as much penicillin as was being produced in the whole of Great Britain.

The Commercial Solvents Corporation was able to by-pass the surface culture method entirely and, taking full advantage of the latest researches, start brewing penicillin straight away by the deep culture process which enabled them to attain a large production before the British producers could fight their way through the maze of difficulties which hemmed them in. Where the American producers could order their new plant and get it delivered in a reasonable time, even the Ministry of Supply with its sweeping powers and all its priorities could not work this miracle in Britain. It was easy enough to give an order and almost impossible to obtain delivery. Indeed in one case some vital freeze-drying plant was not delivered nearly three years after the order was placed.

In the circumstances the British genius for improvising was called into full play. The chemical manufacturers who set out to produce penicillin in Great Britain were compelled to make do with the materials in hand, and this drove them of necessity to adopt the bottle method of production because they could obtain bottles when there was practically no likelihood of obtaining anything else. The great firm of Boots were glad to select ordinary quart milk bottles for their culture vessels, while the Royal Naval Medical Service utilized a pint milk bottle when it started to produce penicillin for the use of the Royal Navy.

It was the Glaxo Laboratories at Greenford which won the distinction of starting up the first full-size penicillin factory in Great Britain, after their research chemists had carefully studied the Oxford paper in 1940 and, in a letter dated October 25, 1940, had made preliminary inquiries at Oxford. In September, 1941, one of the research chemists went up to Oxford to discuss the process with Dr. Chain, at which time Professor Florey was in the United States trying to induce American manufacturers to produce penicillin. The outcome was that the Greenford research chemists consulted Professor Raistrick and began to investigate nine of his strains of *Penicillium notatum* from which they selected one that gave a maximum yield of about twenty units per millilitre.

Neither the culture vessels nor the methods of extracting the penicillin with ether or amyl acetate satisfied the Greenford chemists who, by the end of 1942, had evolved a new method of isolating the penicillin by filtering it through a bed of charcoal superimposed on a layer of kieselguhr. Their new type of culture vessel resembled a glass saucepan, with the sides, top and bottom and hollow handle all blown in one, the handle being used as the spout through which the medium was poured before being sterilized and seeded. Tens of thousands of these Pyrex glass culture flasks were made in time by a few clever craftsmen. The vessels were regarded as superior to milk bottles because the mould could be grown on the same depth of medium over the whole area, whereas in a bottle lying down, the medium was deep in the centre and tapered up to nothing at the sides, thus the fungus at the sides was starved of medium while that growing in the centre had more medium than it could digest, and this resulted in a smaller yield of penicillin than when the depth of the medium was the same over the whole surface. Made of heat-proof glass for sterilizing in the autoclaves, the flasks cost four shillings each, and when I visited the laboratories in January, 1946, I learned that the breakages averaged about one thousand a week, so the weekly wastage of flasks cost about £200.

The same team of scientists who worked out the improved isolation technique also experimented with variations of the chemical medium first used by Raistrick, and by trial and error and the addition and subtraction of various substances were able to increase the yield of penicillin as well as to simplify and improve the method of extraction. The range of immense modern laboratories in which they worked covered acres of floor space, but only with difficulty could a corner be found in which to carry on the penicillin experiments. Concentrating on the problems of production, the senior organic chemist and his colleagues began to produce a little penicillin, not much, but enough to show that their method worked. In December, 1942, their penicillin had a potency of one hundred and thirty units per milligramme, the next batch yielded one hundred and forty units, the third batch jumped to two hundred and sixty units, then there was a falling off to two hundred and to one hundred and fifty units. Very methodically they went on producing small quantities of penicillin, experimenting all the time to improve the yield.

Then one of the research chemists visited Manbre Garton & Co., the starch and glucose manufacturers, where he saw Mr. Jonas Webb, who was then the general manager. "Can you tell me anything about corn-steep liquor?" inquired the chemist.

"Come with me and I will show you," said Mr. Webb, who took the chemist along to show him what corn-steep liquor was like and told him how it varied from batch to batch. Long experience on production with the Corn Products Company in the United States and with the Corn Products Company in Paisley before joining Gartons had given him a knowledge of corn-steep liquor that was unrivalled. From then on there was the fullest co-operation between the two men, Mr. Webb sending along samples of all sorts of corn-steep liquor to Greenford where they were tested by culturing the mould on them to find the best one for producing penicillin, while Gartons tried modifications of their process to make a better corn-steep liquor that would give a higher yield.

Fully alive to the possibilities of penicillin as well as to the difficulties of producing it, the managing director of Glaxo was keenly watching the results of his technicians. Anxious to do everything possible to produce this precious drug to save the wounded, he began quietly gathering one or two people with knowledge of the subject to form the nucleus of a penicillin staff, among them being a botanist from Bristol University. The work of the chemists convinced the management that commercial production was possible, although they were making no more than one hundred litres of penicillin brew a week.

"Can you multiply your present method to give a thousand litres a week?" the chief research chemist was asked.

"Yes, I think so," he said, and the managing director went off to the Ministry of Supply to see if they could find him factory space in which to start up penicillin production on a commercial scale. In normal times it would have been considered unwise to launch out without designing and installing a perfect pilot plant from which the full-scale plant could be designed. But the need for penicillin was so urgent that it was decided to dispense with this procedure and to start on full-scale production as soon as the necessary floor space could be found.

By January, 1943, some vacant floor space had been located by the Ministry. It was in a corner of the big Nestlé Milk Factory at Aylesbury, where a wing previously devoted to making cream cheese was closed owing to the stresses of war, and it was here that the chemists were faced with the task of creating a penicillin factory from nothing. No one could have been more helpful than the factory owners. They allowed the chemists the use of two of their big sterilizers and other useful plant which was a priceless boon in those days when apparatus of the kind was almost unobtainable. Then they were lucky enough to secure the assistance of half a dozen girls who had been trained in the Pasteurization plant of the factory. Drilled in the need of absolute cleanliness, the girls were able without undue trouble to master the technique that was essential to the successful culture of the mould. There were hectic days gathering plant, engaging staff, accepting delivery of culture flasks, planning the floor space for incubator and inoculation room; but quite soon, with the unstinted help of all concerned, the manifold drawbacks were overcome and a start made upon production.

Gradually the brew at Aylesbury was worked up to one thousand litres a day, at which time the brew at Greenford was two hundred litres a day. It is of interest that the first batch from Aylesbury produced seventeen mega* units of penicillin. Of further interest is

One mega unit equals one million Oxford units.

the fact that by the middle of February, 1943, the penicillin produced at Greenford from the time the work was first started amounted in all to 31.8 mega units, which was a considerable production for those days and a tribute to the good work of the chemists. About that time the Greenford production averaged two mega units a day; the Aylesbury production naturally fluctuated, as was to be expected from a newly-installed plant, but it was brought up to between three and four mega units a day, or 3,000,000 and 4,000,000 Oxford units. By March 1, 1943, the chemists had finished the work of starting up the factory, so one of the firm's medical representatives was installed as manager and proved himself an able administrator as long as he was in charge. All these researches and developments were financed by the company which in the aggregate spent several hundred thousand pounds on its penicillin plants at Greenford, Aylesbury and Watford.

In order to gain an idea of the first penicillin factory to be started in Great Britain, I paid a visit to Aylesbury early in 1946. Just inside the big door of the factory was a bare little office, on the wall of which was a long chart showing the ups and downs of penicillin production during the past year. "That's where we cut down the medium," said the manager, indicating the week when the medium in the flasks was nearly halved, with a decided increase in yield and a corresponding saving of medium and costs.

Outside the little office a vast conglomeration of machines all carefully swathed in dust sheets occupied the big concrete floor of the gloomy wing of the building that vanished into the dim recesses on the left. In the nearby corner was a wooden partition of unpainted timber in which I noticed a small matchboard door which my guides unlatched, and I stepped into the earliest penicillin factory to be set up in Britain. There was a hissing of steam. The floor was running with water. A girl sitting in front of a large tank of medium inserted two red rubber tubes into two flasks, she turned a tap to allow the correct amount of medium to run in, then she passed them on to another girl who plugged them with cotton wool before putting them into a wire basket which held twelve.

A few yards away stood two circular autoclaves, six feet in diameter, into which two attendants packed a dozen baskets before clamping down the massive lids and turning on the steam to sterilize the flasks of medium. The steam killed the toughest bacteria. The flasks were then wheeled to a cooling chamber where they remained for twenty-four hours and by the time they were ready to be inoculated their temperature had dropped to twenty-five degrees centigrade.

Close to the cooling chamber was a small chamber with windows along each side, not unlike a portable office on a housing estate. Painted white inside, it was brilliantly illuminated with electric light and supplied with germ-free air through filters. This was the inoculating chamber in which two girls co-operated to seed the medium. They resembled two Tuaregs of the desert in their sterile white caps and gowns and flowing masks covering their faces just below their bright eyes. Lifting a basket of flasks from her trolley outside, a girl pushed it through a trap into the inoculating chamber where the girl inside slid it along some metal rollers to her companion who, using a spray gun fed by gravity from a container full of a spore suspension on a shelf above her head, unplugged the flask, pressed the trigger of the gun to shoot in a dose of spores, plugged the flask slickly and placed it back into the basket. After seeding a dozen flasks in quick time, she pushed the basket along the rollers for a girl outside the other end of the chamber to collect through a trap and place on a carrier for conveyance to the incubator.

The incubator was a large concrete place controlled thermostatically, with heating bars and fans, so that when the temperature rose too high the heat was cut off and the fans switched on, and when it dropped too low more heating bars came into operation, consequently the temperature could be controlled to within half a degree. In aisle after aisle were stacked tens of thousands of flasks. Chalked upon each wooden rack was the date on which the flasks were inoculated and I noticed that the batches were rather mixed, with the newest batches resembling brown sherry placed between batches in which the mould was white or turning blue. This arrangement was based on experience. After four days of growth, the mould raised the temperature inside the flasks a degree or two higher than the temperature outside, so the new flasks were placed between the older flasks to gain the benefit of this extra heat.

The scientists here studied the vagaries of the mould to such good purpose that they were able to increase the yield by varying the temperature at different stages of growth. How they accomplished this in an incubator wherein batches of mould of all ages grew side by side was their technical secret. But they managed it, with the result that this first penicillin factory became most efficient, producing in its best weeks penicillin with a potency ranging from seven hundred and fifty to nine hundred units per milligramme—a potency sometimes beaten by the Stratford factory which touched one thousand units per milligramme. This was two thirds the potency of the pure sodium salt of penicillin which is rated at 1,667 units.

A million units of penicillin is known as a mega unit, and the improvised Aylesbury factory was worked up by the end of 1945 to produce eight hundred mega units a week. The penicillin was extracted by filtering it through powdered charcoal, from which it was extracted by washing with water before adding chloroform. After further treatment it was sent to the Greenford laboratories for the final extraction and drying.

One thing they learned at Aylesbury was that the solution of penicillin does not like travelling. They were very puzzled at first by the discrepancy between the potency of the penicillin extract loaded on the lorry at Aylesbury and the potency on its arrival at Greenford. The figure given by the chemist in charge at Aylesbury was always about ten per cent stronger than the potency measured by the chemist at Greenford. They could not understand it. That both potencies could be correct was hardly credible. Yet in fact they were, for careful checking revealed that a tenth of the elusive penicillin's potency vanished on the road. The change in temperature during the journey destroyed it.

There was also a mysterious loss of potency in the Watford factory where a second plant was started on the fifth floor of the British Rubber Hose Company. For five days a week the heavy machinery pounded away on the other floors of the factory, setting up a vibration that was most marked on the fifth floor. On these five days the potency was always ten per cent less than on the two days during the week-end when the machinery was stopped and the factory free of vibration. Checking and counter-checking for six months indicated that the vibration set up by the machinery affected the newly-inoculated flasks in such a way as to cause some of the spores to sink and thus lessen the yield, while during the Saturday and Sunday when the machinery was not running the spores remained undisturbed on the surface of the medium and were able to grow sufficiently to overcome the effects of the agitation when the machinery started up again.

In this Watford factory, which was run when I saw it by three young scientists who graduated in chemistry at Glasgow University, a remarkable team spirit grew up among all the workers from the technical chiefs to the cleaners. The whole of the floor space was fully occupied by the plant and it was impossible to expand production by adding further units. The one way in which production could be expanded was by extracting a higher percentage of penicillin from the brew. This called for an all-round increase of efficiency, and to foster it the whole staff were given the chance of earning efficiency pay. Each week the amount of penicillin that could be extracted was fixed as a target, and every unit above this target earned the staff efficiency pay. It was not possible to extract every unit of penicillin from the brew; unavoidable wastages were bound to occur; but efficiency pay cut the losses to a minimum and gave all the workers something extra to work for. The target was pinned up for all to see, and during my visit I saw that it had already been exceeded and was registering a nice balance for the staff.

The technical manager was a wise man. He insisted that all should share in the efficiency pay, that the cleaners by keeping the place scrupulously clean and removing any possible cause of contamination could contribute as much to the output as the chief chemist. They worked as a team and if one careless worker did anything to lessen the output he or she soon heard about it from the other workers who in this way kept each other up to the mark. Chalked upon a blackboard were the daily statistics, how many flasks had been handled, the number with wet plugs of cotton wool, the number contaminated, the number broken. The figures were remarkable, only nineteen flasks contaminated out of ten thousand, while one day the workers excelled themselves with only one flask contaminated. The staff could see at a glance what they were doing and where they were losing output.

Moving belts were installed here to deal with the baskets of flasks, for the day's batch of ten thousand flasks could not be handled otherwise. As soon as the flasks were charged with medium and plugged, the baskets were piled in an electric carrier suspended from an overhead rail and each basket was roofed with a bent piece of tin to prevent the plugs from getting wet in the autoclave. By touching a switch, the operator could bring the carrier to a stop in front of any one of the six big autoclaves which were served by a team of six men. Each autoclave had on the wall an electric recorder which marked in ink the rise and fall of the temperature inside the autoclave, thus ensuring that the flasks were properly sterilized.

At Aylesbury the hot flasks were allowed twenty-four hours to cool down. Here they travelled partly submerged on their moving bands through long tanks of water which cooled them to the correct temperature by the time they reached the inoculation room, where the operators inoculated them with a spray gun. Within half an hour of the flasks being removed from the autoclaves, they were cooled and inoculated and a whole day was saved in the process.

The incubator here was enormous. It seemed interminable. And the thousands of flasks resembled thousands of iced cakes stacked in walls, some with white icing and some with blue-green icing. It was remarkably impressive.

To such an art had the chemists reduced their methods of testing and checking that they could usually trace the cause of every contamination. At one time they were mystified by the sterility of a pair of flasks in an occasional basket, and after checking along the line they found it was caused by an operator so keen to get on with her job that she inoculated the flasks too quickly after flaming the barrel of the spray gun, consequently the spores passing down the hot barrel were killed by the heat. Another time the research workers were amazed to see some flies flying about in one of the flasks. How they got there was a mystery. In practice and theory nothing could have survived the intense sterilization by steam, yet there were the flies to mock them. Somehow the larvae got into the flask, completed their life cycle and emerged as flies while the mould was growing. The queer thing was that the flask was not contaminated; its penicillin was as potent as the rest in the flasks of that batch. Theoretically it could not happen, but it did.

The young Scottish chemist in charge of the extraction plant was an enthusiast like everyone else. He led me to the cold room in which the penicillin extracts were stored. Dipping into a container, he held up a glass of liquid resembling brown sherry. "This is the first extract," he said, and dipping into another container, held up a sample resembling pale sherry. "This is the second extract."

These extracts were sent to the Greenford Laboratories to be turned into powder in the battery of freeze-drying machines with their vacuum pumps and electric controls before being packed for use. At Greenford was the spore farm in charge of a young scientist who performed the important duties of culturing the mould for use in the factories and of testing the corn-steep liquor so that she could make up a medium to yield the maximum potency. The master culture of the mould was freeze-dried in sand or dried plasma and stored in small glass ampoules, from which a few grains of sand or plasma were taken with a needle and placed on a slope of molasses agar at the bottom of a culture tube. In due course the spores clinging to the plasma or sand developed into circular blue-green colonies with a narrow white fringe. Sometimes a shadowy streak or wedge grew in the colony, to be detected and discarded at once by the scientist who knew that the mould was mutating.

The tubes of colonies containing countless millions of spores were sent to the factories where they were used for inoculating full-size flasks. Directly these flasks were covered with sporing mould, a quantity of distilled water and a few glass beads were placed in them, a dozen flasks were packed into a wooden rocker upon the floor and the operator rocked the flasks with her foot. This action made the beads roll about on the mould from which the spores were soon separated and left suspended in the water, which in its turn was transferred to containers to be used for inoculating the thousands of flasks in which the penicillin was brewed.

It might be expected that when the formula was fixed, there would be nothing to do but measure out the same quantities of chemicals and mix them in the same way over and over again for ever. But each delivery of corn-steep liquor varied in its chemical constituents. The result was that if the exact quantities of chemicals and corn-steep liquor were mixed, the medium was never exactly the same, owing to the variations in the corn-steep liquor. To overcome this difficulty and ensure that the mould was grown upon the medium giving the biggest yield of penicillin, the chemist in charge tested each delivery of corn-steep liquor and mixed up thirty-two different media on which the mould was grown in one hundred and ninety-two flasks. The medium giving the highest yield was then used by the factories for that particular lot of corn-steep liquor, while the managers were advised of the yield obtainable and efficiency payments were earned on all units harvested above this figure.

"The operators are so keen that they never hide mistakes," I was told. "If they should happen to make a slip, they at once ring up to say so and ask the chemist how to put it right."

While these workers were making penicillin at Aylesbury and Watford and Stratford and Greenford, a modern factory under the technical control of Dr. A. H. Campbell, Ph.D., was starting up at Barnard Castle in Durham to make penicillin by the latest deep culture method that was destined to supersede these factories and make them redundant.

It was not possible here to give a detailed account of the efforts of all the famous pharmaceutical firms who have taken part in the penicillin campaign and, in the circumstances, no comparison between them would be fair. No more than a general description of the two principal types of production could be attempted. It must in justice be realized that every firm in a position to enter this field during the war played a most useful part and loyally observed the directions given by the Government in the early stages to obtain production by the quickest method, even if the method adopted seemed likely to be succeeded by something newer. In some cases the firms concerned experimented with new methods while carrying on production by the tried method, with the result that there were many interesting developments.

Such firms as Boots, Ltd., working in a magnificent new factory that was erected at Nottingham, and Burroughs Wellcome and Co., who installed a fine plant in their new building at Beckenham, operated the bottle method of surface culture, as did British Drug Houses; but Imperial Chemical Industries, in addition to the bottle method, operated the open-tray surface culture in which the trays of culture were housed in a huge horizontal incubator resembling a boiler. Naturally the scientists and chemical engineers in these factories were aware of all the main lines of development and they adapted their methods to solve their own particular problems.

An unexpected and tremendous demand for penicillin was created by the discovery in the United States that the drug could be used for the treatment of syphilis, which is caused by a spiral-shaped micro-organism known as a spirochaete. It was in Washington in 1943 that Dr. Mahoney, of Staten Island Hospital, New York, announced to the National Research Committee that he had successfully tested penicillin against a spirochaetal infection in rabbits and had then treated five human cases of primary syphilis. Giving each man injections totalling 1,200,000 units, he had found that the blood test became negative in five weeks. This announcement was received with amazement and almost disbelief, for few doctors could credit that penicillin would be effective in two such different infections as gonorrhæa and syphilis.

Little was said on the subject, because the doctors were afraid that the news might increase the incidence of venereal disease. Events justified this judgment, for not only did cases relapse, but men deliberately laid themselves open to reinfection, despite the warnings of their doctors, under the impression that penicillin would soon put them right again. The truth is that the periodic cycles of this disease make it impossible to state with certainty for some years whether penicillin will provide a permanent cure for syphilis.

This discovery naturally led to many clinical tests in the United

States as well as in Great Britain, and in December, 1945, some of the American results were published in *Nature* by Dr. James Marshall who stated: "Some patients with venereal diseases are already treating their condition in the most light-hearted manner and repeatedly re-expose themselves to infection as soon as they think themselves cured. If penicillin were indeed a one hundred per cent cure such people would harm only themselves; but unfortunately this is not the case."

In the tests on syphilis in the United States the physicians gave doses of penicillin varying from 60,000 units up to 1,200,000 units, and found that intra-muscular injections every three hours were the best method of administration. Every patient relapsed who had only 60,000 units; seventy-five per cent relapsed who had 300,000 units; forty per cent relapsed who had 600,000 units; and from fifteen to twenty per cent relapsed who had 1,200,000 units. Some patients were given thirty injections in four days, but the results were not so good as when the same quantity of penicillin was spread over seven and a half days. The present practice is to inject every three hours for seven and a half days a total of 2,400,000 units; but Dr. Marshall says that even when this amount of penicillin was injected in early cases of syphilis, between seven per cent and eight per cent of the cases kept under observation for six months in Great Britain were found to relapse. That is why it is essential to treat the matter with caution.

The latest penicillin factory at Speke, near Liverpool, may truthfully be described as colossal. In the first place, this factory is the largest in the world, larger than anything operating in the United States. Built by the Government with the money of the British people, it is managed by the Distillers Company. Here, also, the war slowed down the building of the factory as well as the manufacture of the plant, and it was not possible to start up production until the last days of 1945, when the first brew yielded its penicillin on December 21.

A car ride of about fifteen minutes from the centre of Liverpool brought me to this great secret factory with its barbed wire and unscalable metal fences to keep out unwanted visitors, and as we turned in at the gate a gang of men were busy laying another section of a tarmac road where a short while ago was a quagmire. In those days only the foolhardy ventured outside the buildings without gumboots; now the hard roads were nearing completion and I could walk round without soiling my shoes.

To the left of the main gate lay the single storey brick building housing the office staff and canteen. To the right of the gate were the gatehouse and surgery, and separated by one of the internal roadways was the main building containing laboratories, the cooker room, the seed room and the fermenter room with the fermentation tanks. The main building was about three hundred feet long and eighty feet high, built of hard brick set in cement, as were all the other buildings. At right angles to the fermentation building, across the road at the back, lay the big machinery and compressor house, and adjacent to it was the building in which the penicillin brew was filtered and concentrated. The freeze-drying, packing and storing were done in another large building set at right angles. Many workmen were engaged on a multiplicity of jobs, laying roads, using oxy-acetylene cutters, plastering here, lagging pipes there, fitting metal frames and fixing glass walls to sterile rooms. But the factory was so immense that the workmen were hardly noticed.

The factory itself occupied a site of eleven and a half acres in the midst of green fields, so the air was fairly free of bacteria. During my visit in mid-February, 1946, the production was already running to between six thousand and ten thousand mega units a week, with a potency of between three hundred and five hundred units per milli-gramme. The plant was planned to produce twenty thousand mega units, or twenty thousand million units, a week, and this output will undoubtedly be exceeded as modifications take place in the process.

Walking over to the fermentation building to make the acquaintance of the Process Superintendent, I saw a great mobile tank which had just arrived by road that morning from Paisley, pumping into the storage tanks its load of 2,300 gallons of corn-steep liquor. Six huge grey cylinders reached into the sky, each holding eight thousand gallons of liquid; two contained corn-steep liquor, two amyl acetate and two acetone, which were all consumed in prodigious quantities. The load of corn-steep liquor that was being pumped into the tank would last no more than a month.

The store room on the ground floor was piled with sacks containing various substances, including lactose, lime and a wax-like substance which prevented the brew from foaming and causing a troublesome scum. These things, combined with corn-steep liquor and water, were the ingredients of the medium which was prepared in the cooker room in two giant cylinders, twelve feet in diameter, which each held ten thousand gallons and towered up and up toward the roof. A hot-water storage tank of similar size and capacity was supported in a horizontal position overhead. After the medium was mixed, the mash was cooked and sterilized under steam pressure for an hour while metal paddles resembling the three-bladed propellers of a motor boat whirled continuously to keep the mash in a state of agitation. From the cooking tanks, the mash could be forced either to the seed tank room or the fermentation hall as desired.

Above the office of the Process Superintendent were the laboratories in which the chemists and their assistants cultured the mould, while in a range of laboratories on the other side of the corridor their colleagues tested the batches of penicillin fluid to discover its potency and to see that it contained nothing harmful. The chemists here did not start the spores growing on the agar medium adopted elsewhere. Instead they used chips of yellow maize as a dry medium. A thin layer of this dry medium was spread over the bottom of conical flasks and seeded with the spores of the mould. The flasks were then placed on the shelves of the incubating room for four days to allow the spores to develop. A little liquid medium was then added and the flasks were placed in a shaking machine which jogged them backwards and forwards for two days, during which the colonies of the mould made steady growth. To enable the colonies to multiply, the contents of each flask were then transferred with additional medium into much larger flasks with long necks, and these in their turn were shaken in the shaking-machine for two more days before being taken to the seed tank room where each flask was used to seed a tank holding about five hundred gallons of mash, the long necks of the flasks fitting into rubber connectors for emptying into the seed tanks.

So far, the shaking of the bottles had aerated the medium to enable the spores to grow freely. But the fourteen cylindrical seed tanks with their maze of steam pipes, air pipes and water pipes were necessarily fixed in one place and could not be shaken. Yet to enable each spore to grow freely, it was essential to provide it with air, not only those spores at the top of the mash, but also the myriad of spores submerged in the middle of the mash, all demanded air to produce their maximum growth and highest yield of penicillin. The problem of supplying air to the submerged spores was solved by blowing purified air through the mash. When grown in this way, the mould did not form a solid mat, as when grown on the surface of the medium in bottles or trays, but each spore produced a small globular mass of growth. For two days the spores were allowed to grow in the seed tanks, when they were ready to be forced through the pipe line to the fermentation tanks, ten days after the spores were first seeded on the dry medium.

Everything about the fermentation room was gigantic. Human beings were dwarfed inside it. The room itself was about one hundred and forty feet long and sixty feet high, with a central gangway flanked on each side by a row of seven fermentation tanks. They were overwhelming, all lagged and jacketed, so that cooling could be carried out with refrigerated water in the surrounding jacket if the fermenting mould tended to raise the temperature above the production limit. As I gazed upon these great tanks, I could not help comparing them with Heatley's small culture vessel and I was lost in wonder at the progress made in five years. To paraphrase Mr. Winston Churchill, never in the history of medicine has so much been accomplished so quickly by so many. The discovery of penicillin was a triumph of British scientific co-operation; the production of penicillin at Speke marked the triumphant co-operation of British and American scientists and chemical engineers working whole-heartedly in a common cause for a common end. Each contributed to a common pool all his knowledge and experience and skill and Mankind will for ever be indebted to them.

Climbing the metal stairs leading from the ground floor to the top deck was like climbing from the engine-room of a liner. Through this concrete deck emerged the tops of the fourteen fermentation tanks to finish off in two long lines of domes each measuring a dozen feet across, fitted with a galaxy of pipes and stopcocks of various sizes. Overhead ran the big air trunkway and many other pipes for various purposes, branching at regular intervals to serve the tanks. From the pipes of a giant tank nearby came the sound of hissing steam to tell that the tank and all its pipes were being sterilized for the next brew. Glancing over the rail of the top deck to the floor far below, I saw a pygmy workman dragging in a lead, and within a minute or two he had donned dark goggles and a protective mask which made him resemble a Martian, and the scene was suddenly lit by the vivid light of his oxy-acetylene cutter as the sparks began to fly.

Descending from the top deck to the ground floor again, I watched an operator turn a stopcock in a fermentation tank. There was a burst of steam to sterilize the pipe, then another gentle turn of a stopcock brought forth a trickle of liquid of a slightly greenish tinge. Placing his hand under the trickle, the operator held it out to me full of penicillin brew, a mass of globules of mould, all soft and steaming.

OPPOSITE: *Sterile rooms in the world's largest penicillin factory at Speke, lit by ultra-violet light and with ceilings and walls of glass on which bacteria cannot lodge. The operators in plastic visors and sterile clothing are filling bottles with fluid penicillin above and placing rubber caps on the bottles below.*

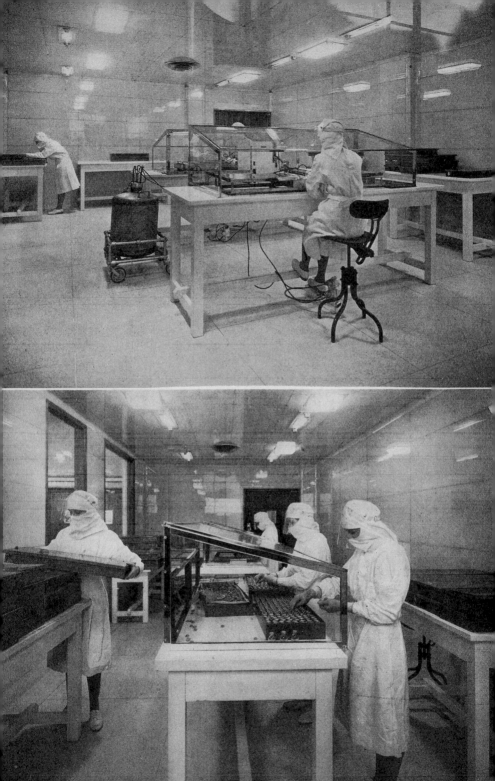

"It's nearly ready," he said, as he turned on the sterilizing steam again to prevent any risk of contamination, and by now the penicillin in that brew has probably saved lives.

Leaving the fermentation hall, I glanced inside the engine house where three air compressors, with their six thousand volt motors developing five hundred horsepower, were each dealing with two thousand five hundred cubic feet of air a minute, sucking it through six tall air shafts containing the filters to trap the bacteria and make the air sterile. Then I crossed the road to the filtration room to which the fermented beer, as the penicillin brew is termed, was pumped across from the fermentation tanks. The concrete floor was saturated with lysol to trap all germs from air or shoes, and here the mould was filtered out and thrown away, while the medium containing the penicillin was chilled and pumped to large tanks. From now on, all the tanks were made of stainless steel or else lined with deep blue glass reminiscent of the linings of old-fashioned silver salt cellars. Curious to know how they managed to line the tanks in this way, I learned that the tanks were made white hot before being sprayed all over the inside with powdered glass which fused on the hot metal and formed an impermeable sheet of glass.

Mounting the steel steps to the concrete floor through which the tops of the tanks emerged, I found a sooty film all round. Bags full of black powder were stacked on the floor, a sooty powder which was in fact charcoal costing a large sum per ton, and an operator, opening a manhole in the top of the tank, emptied half a ton of it into the cold penicillin fluid below. This charcoal, which absorbed the penicillin from the medium, was filtered out by forcing the fluid under a pressure of eighty pounds to the square inch through a giant plate and frame filter seven feet long, containing sixty-five filter cloths. Various conversions and re-conversions brought the concentrated penicillin fluid at last to a stainless steel tank in which I saw it "boiling" away in a high vacuum at a temperature of ninety-four degrees Fahrenheit, or one hundred and eighteen degrees less than the temperature at which water normally boils. This final concentration of penicillin fluid was transferred to a stainless steel carboy to await its turn to be freeze-dried in the sterile rooms after samples had passed the tests.

Adjoining the sterile rooms was the bottle-washing room in which an ingenious machine enabled four girls to wash forty thousand little bottles a day. Packed in metal boxes, the bottles were loaded into

OPPOSITE: *Above are thousands of flasks travelling slowly through the three long tanks of water to cool them down in half an hour for inoculation, thus speeding up the Glaxo bottle process by a whole day. Below is the freeze-drying vacuum plant, resembling a battery of armour-plated refrigerators, in the wonderful national Ministry of Supply Penicillin Factory at Speke*

four sterilizers in which they were sterilized during the night, and next morning the girls in the sterile room opened the doors on their side of the sterilizing cabinets and took out the bottles to fill them.

Entry into the sterile rooms was of course forbidden to all except the operators who underwent the routine of passing through the dressing rooms, sterilizing their hands and donning sterile rubber gloves and robes and caps before putting on dark goggles and a special plastic vizor to protect their eyes from the light of the ultra-violet lamps with which the ceilings of the sterile rooms are fitted. The walls and ceilings were of glass, and every known precaution was taken to exclude germs. This was why the sterilizing cabinets had doors for loading in the bottle-washing room and doors for unloading in the sterile room. It was also the reason why the carboys of penicillin fluid were brought to a small recess in the bottle-washing room and connected with a pipe running through the wall of the sterile room to the Seitz filter, through the twenty asbestos pads of which the penicillin fluid was forced for final filtration and sterilization before being bottled.

Identification marks enabled the chemists to keep track of each bottle of penicillin and trace its progress from the time it was bottled until it was packed. The bottles packed in their metal boxes were frozen and conveyed to the drying room which contained a battery of twenty-six drying cabinets with black and white control wheels. The drying cabinets of white enamel resembled ordinary domestic refrigerators, but their temperature touched a hundred degrees of frost in a high vacuum to accomplish the feat of transforming the frozen penicillin fluid into powder. Sometimes the drying penicillin bubbled up into a spherical mass at the bottom of the bottle and set solid in this form, but a sharp tap on the bottle soon reduced the bubble to powder.

After the drying process, the bottles passed in their covered metal trays to the stoppering room where the nimble fingers of the rubber-gloved operators slipped the rubber caps over the bottles which then glided along in single file to the capping machine which sealed them with a metal cap before they were repacked and locked in their metal boxes for storage in the cold room, a place so vast that one would swear it could never be filled, yet the Speke factory could fill it in six weeks.

This great national factory, paid for by the British people, was brought into being by the co-operation of many scientists and chemical engineers on both sides of the Atlantic and with a staff of less than four hundred highly-skilled chemists and technical operators it can produce penicillin at a price comparable with any. So from that lucky day when Fleming first saw the mould on his agar plate, we have followed through all its astonishing vicissitudes the gradual development and isolation and purification of penicillin until the gigantic factory at Speke materialized as the world's finest monument to the most miraculous drug discovered by Man.

The capital expenditure on penicillin plants in the United Kingdom, including the early surface-culture plants and the later deep-culture plants, was about £3,100,000, of which about £2,300,000 was financed by the British Government and the remainder by private enterprise.

The production of penicillin in Great Britain during 1943 averaged only 300 mega units a month. In 1944 British production was raised to an average of 3,166 mega units a month, while America leapt ahead to an average of 131,115 mega units a month, or more than forty times the British output. Fighting against manifold war difficulties, which the United States were most fortunately spared, the British producers managed to force up their average production in 1945 to 26,000 mega units a month, compared with the average American production of 587,698 mega units a month, so although there was still a big difference in the output of the two countries, the British producers made better progress and succeeded in reducing the gap from forty times as great to twenty-two times as great.

The early months of 1946 saw a steep increase in production on both sides of the Atlantic, with the United States practically trebling its output which averaged 1,555,000 mega units a month for the first three months of the year, against which Great Britain, benefiting from the advantages of its two superb new deep-culture plants, pushed up production in the month of April to 260,000 mega units, or ten times the monthly average for 1945. Though she still lagged behind, Great Britain began to make relatively greater progress in production than the United States, and so far as quality was concerned, much of the British penicillin was over 1,000 units per milligramme and fully equal to the best produced in America.

The big jump in American production during the first three months of 1946 was due to a new deep-culture mould found in Peoria and developed in the two universities of Minnesota and Wisconsin, a mould so productive that it yielded about twice as much penicillin as the best of the moulds which it has now superseded. These new American strains of the mould were not put into production at Speke and Barnard Castle until the beginning of May, 1946, after which date the British output mounted rapidly until it had reached 363,724 mega units in July, 1946.

During the war years the sole interest of the British and American Governments was to obtain penicillin for the treatment of the fighting forces and the price was a secondary consideration. But the relaxation of control by the Ministry of Supply in Great Britain brought into play the normal economic factors which made it impossible for the early bottle-plants to compete with the latest deep-culture plants, with the result that in June, 1946, the bottle plants run by the Imperial Chemical Industries, Boots, British Drug Houses, Glaxo, and Burroughs, Wellcome became redundant and the new factories had to close down. Against any financial loss involved must be set the life-saving purpose they served in our dire emergency.

Initially, penicillin cost many pounds per mega unit, but the success of the gigantic deep-culture plants at Speke and Barnard Castle so increased output and decreased costs that the Ministry of Supply were able to arrange for the distribution of the drug through ordinary trade channels for sale by the chemists on production of a doctor's certificate at £1 per mega unit of a million units; the prices for lesser quantities were 2s. 9d. for 100,000 units; 4s. 9d. for 200,000 units and 10s. 6d. for 500,000 units, prices that were lower than prices then current in the United States.

Thus after a terrific struggle against war-time restrictions and limited resources, the penicillin producers of the United Kingdom were able to overcome their handicaps and compete in the economic field with the American producers.

The first phase of penicillin production came to an end with the closing down of the new bottle factories which in some cases were operating for little more than a year, yet so great and rapid were the technical developments that in this short time they became obsolete.

The coming into production of the deep-culture plants in Great Britain marked the beginning of the second phase of penicillin production.

Whether there will be a third phase of synthetic production remains to be seen. The progress achieved in the past few years by British and American scientists in their secret researches that were designed to solve the many baffling chemical problems of making synthetic penicillin may now be disclosed in the Appendix.

APPENDIX

The lifting of the official ban on the publication of information concerning the synthesis of penicillin makes it possible to touch on this aspect of the subject in this Appendix. But the matter is so complex and highly technical that no attempt can be made to do more than give a general picture of the accomplishments of the chemists who have been devoting themselves to this task for so long. To further this most important work a plan was adopted in December, 1943, for a free interchange of knowledge between the scientists of Great Britain and those of the United States and every scientist and pharmaceutical laboratory so engaged was placed under a seal of secrecy not to reveal what they were doing, the position between the two countries being clarified by a retrospective Agreement that was signed in Washington on January 25, 1946.

Up to the spring of 1946, about seven hundred scientific reports in all had been written by the scientists engaged in attempting the synthesis of penicillin, and it is generally agreed that the drug possesses an entirely new kind of chemical formula. What are known as the ring formulæ have gained their names because of the way the molecules are grouped in a ring, and such formulæ are quite familiar to the chemist. Now penicillin has a ring formula, but what is quite new about it is a special arrangement of atoms in a ring under tension, and the chemists have found it extremely difficult to make the two ends of the broken ring meet. Until they can make the ends of the ring meet with certainty and ease, there is little prospect of penicillin being made synthetically in the laboratory. And even when they make it, there is no certainty that it will be economic to do so. Some of our cleverest chemists have doubted whether the penicillin produced by natural culture methods will ever be superseded by the synthetic product, owing to the cost; other scientists who regard the large number of natural substances that are now made synthetically in the laboratories are inclined to be more hopeful about penicillin.

At Oxford, where Sir Robert Robinson, Professor Wilson Baker, Dr. Chain and Dr. Abraham have been working to synthesize penicillin, there seems to be little doubt that they actually obtained small traces of it in 1944, although their later efforts were not always consistent, for sometimes they succeeded in obtaining a trace of penicillin and sometimes they did not. On the other hand, the American workers have more recently been able to obtain slight traces of penicillin consistently every time.

The Oxford chemists succeeded in breaking up penicillin into various fragments, and in the course of this work they discovered a new amino acid which they named penicillamine. This part of penicillin can be made synthetically in the laboratory without much difficulty—it can be done quite quickly. The other part of the molecule may be isolated in different forms which depend solely on the way the penicillin is treated. If, for instance, penicillin is treated with mercuric chloride in ether and then with alkali, the second part of the molecule is isolated in the form of a ring compound called an oxazolone, a fact which was discovered in the Merck Laboratories in the United States. The oxazolone can also be made synthetically without much difficulty. Although penicillamine and oxazolone can be made synthetically in the laboratory, there has hitherto been extreme difficulty in making both substances join together or unite to form penicillin, yet both these substances contain between them all the atoms that make up a molecule of penicillin.

The chemists in England and America learned that if they made some oxazolone and heated it in pyridine along with penicillamine, they obtained traces of activity resembling that of penicillin. The traces were very, very slight, so infinitesimal that the chemists have been prevented, up to the time of writing, from carrying out the experiments they wished to perform. But their reasons for thinking that they have actually made traces of penicillin are fairly strong. For instance, these traces of activity are destroyed by all the chemical reagents which destroy the activity of penicillin. As the things which destroy penicillin are very numerous, this evidence by itself is very favourable. The synthetic traces of activity are also destroyed by penicillinase, which is an enzyme. The chemists know and have proved that enzymes are so specific, otherwise so selective, that they will generally act upon one substance only, and they may in fact be even more selective than that. For instance, a substance may be made up of crystals that are identical in every way except that the faces of some of the crystals turn to the right, and are known as right-handed, while others turn to the left and are known as left-handed. By some extraordinary selective action a specific enzyme may destroy all the right-handed crystals and leave the left-handed crystals untouched, so the chemists have good reason for believing that because the enzyme known as penicillinase destroys the traces of the active substance which they can make in the laboratory, then that active substance is probably penicillin.

There is another reason for thinking that the chemists have made traces of penicillin in the laboratory. If they obtain their traces of active substance by using synthetic penicillamine in which the sulphur is radio-active, and if they then add a big excess of natural penicillin to the synthetic traces of penicillin containing the radio-active sulphur, they can go on purifying and crystallizing the peni-cillin again and again and each time they find traces of the radio-active sulphur in the penicillin. Just as the air-gunner by using tracer bullets can see where his bullets are going, so scientists by using radio-active sulphur can see where the compound goes, for they can easily measure the radio-activity afterwards. It is argued that if the traces of the synthetic penicillin and the natural penicillin were in fact two different substances, it ought to be possible to separate the synthetic substance with its radio-active sulphur from the natural penicillin. As this cannot be done, it suggests that both substances are identical.

The traces of this active substance hitherto obtained in the laboratory are so small, about one unit per milligramme, that the making of penicillin in the laboratory on an economic scale does not seem very feasible. Yet it must always be borne in mind that what the scientists cannot do to-day, they may well achieve to-morrow. One or two chemists, who ought to know, do not feel very hopeful. Their doubts may be understood when it is known that penicillin is now being made in Great Britain of a quality so high that it averages about 1,500 units per milligramme, while the potency of some batches rises to 1,620 units, which is only a few units less than that of the purest crystalline sodium salt of Penicillin 2, which has a potency of 1,667 units per milligramme. It may be recorded that the pure crystalline sodium salt of Penicillin 2, of a potency ranging from 1,650 to 1,667 units per milligramme, that was to serve as the international standard of purity against which all penicillins could be tested, was supplied to the International Bureau of Standards in part by British chemical manufacturers and in part by American manufacturers. Ever since the British chemists succeeded in producing pure crystalline penicillin, they have continued to increase its production from the surface culture brew and also from the deep culture brew at Speke and Barnard Castle. It gives some indication of the immense strides made in Great Britain after the end of the war.

In America, the firm of Chas. Pfizer was for years producing chemical compounds by the deep-culture technique of fermenta-tion before making penicillin by the surface-culture method; and

directly the deep culture of penicillin became commercially possible
it built a factory costing £600,000 in the record time of twenty-two
weeks, with giant fermenters which now produce penicillin of an
average potency of 1,300 units to 1,400 units per milligramme, while
a crystalline sodium salt of Penicillin G is also produced with a
potency of 1,600 units per milligramme. As already mentioned,
the Commercial Solvents Corporation of Indiana started to make
penicillin straight away by the deep-culture method, and their
development programme indicated what could be accomplished by
drive and initiative. The research chemists did not begin their
deep-culture experiments until June 1943; by August the design was
started of a large-scale plant upon which construction was begun on
September 15, 1943, and by January 31, 1944, the first fermenter was
set. The potency of the initial batches of penicillin varied between
300 units and 700 units per milligramme, and the latest potencies
range from 1,300 to 1,650 units per milligramme. The firm's
research chemists were successful in achieving crystalline penicillin
which required no refrigeration and was remarkably stable under
heat—improvements in the drug which were also effected by British
chemists some time ago. Incidentally, the Commercial Solvents
Corporation supplied the technical and engineering information
which fructified as the world's largest penicillin factory at Speke,
and the American company was given an option to purchase a
minority interest in this great British factory if the British Government ever sought to dispose of it.

To the many chances that have influenced the whole history of
penicillin must be added one more lucky chance which led to the
latest and most productive mould of all for deep culture. It happened
that a housewife in Peoria, who noticed that a cantaloupe melon
was growing mouldy where the stalk joined the fruit, was sufficiently
interested to give the melon to the Northern Research Laboratory
in Peoria, where Dr. Kenneth Raper and Mrs. Dorothy Alexander
started cultures from this blue-green mould, and at length isolated
a strain that was labelled N.R.R.L. 1951 B 25. Treating this mould
with X-rays, Dr. M. Demerec, of the Carnegie Institute, Long Island,
induced it to undergo changes or mutations, of which he sent a
large number to the University of Minnesota, where Professor C. M.
Christensen and his associates tested over two thousand before
selecting one which gave them 150 units of penicillin per millilitre in
deep culture. Labelling this strain X 1612, because it was induced
by X-rays, they sent it to the University of Wisconsin, where

Professor W. H. Peterson and Professor M. H. Johnson confirmed that X 1612 produced substantially higher yields than any other known strain. Greatly improved, it was passed into general use to increase the production of penicillin. Thus, to the observant and intelligent housewife of Peoria the world owes the discovery of the highest-yielding mould for deep culture so far discovered.

Whether penicillin will prove to be as beneficial in animal diseases as in human diseases remains to be seen. Up to the present the few cases of bovine mastitis so far treated have shown promising results.

It is fitting to close this book with the chemical formula of the miracle drug, and with a list of the germs which are sensitive to it. In dealing with the Oxford work on the chemistry of the drug, on February 16, 1946, Professor Wilson Baker described the molecule of penicillin as remarkable both chemically and biologically. "As the result of a long series of researches carried out both in this country and in the U.S.A., the structure of penicillin has been almost certainly established as a fuzed thiazolidine β-lactam ring system," he said, and gave the following formula.

$$Me_2C\text{---}CH\text{---}CO_2H$$

$$
\begin{array}{cc}
S & N \\
\backslash & / \\
CH & C=O \\
\backslash & / \\
CH & \\
| & \\
NH.CO.R &
\end{array}
$$

And here is a list of the "microbial enemies of man" which are sensitive to penicillin: *Gonococcus, Meningococcus, Streptococcus haemolyticus, Streptococcus viridans, Pneumococcus, Staphylococcus, Clostridium tetanus, Clostridium Welchii, Corynebacterium diphtheriae, Actinomyces bovis, Spirochaeta pallida, Clostridium septique,* and *Clostridium oedematiens.*

Index